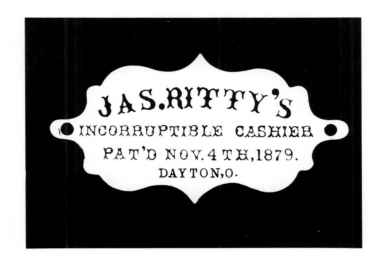

Early Cash Register Chronology©

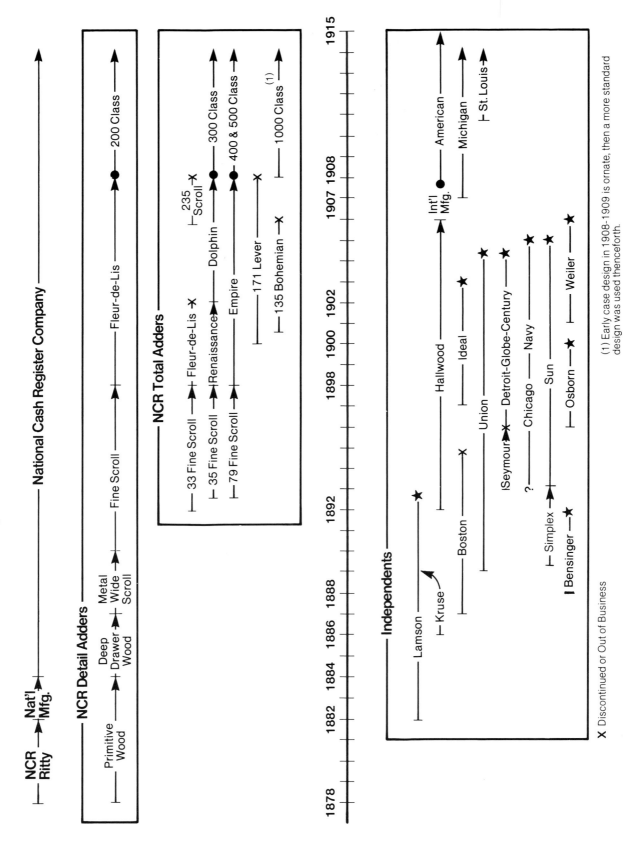

X Discontinued or Out of Business

★ Acquired by NCR

● Case design continued, new model designation

(1) Early case design in 1908-1909 is ornate, then a more standard design was used thenceforth.

© Copyright R. L. Crandall, 1985

The Incorruptible Cashier

Vol. I: The formation of an industry 1876–1890

by Richard L. Crandall
and Sam Robins

The Vestal Press Ltd.
P.O. Box 97
Vestal, New York 13851-0097

Early Cash Register Chronology frontispiece chart artwork by Pat Peck.

Main Photo: Ritty's Incorruptible Cashier. The first commercial cash register invented by John Ritty in 1879 in Dayton, Ohio. His business became the starting point for the formation of the National Cash Register company in 1884. p. 22. **Lower Left: National Cash Register Model 3 "deep-drawer" register.** This all-walnut register with burl insets and brass inlays was one of the earliest National high-style designs. The drawer was sized to include a coin tray identical in size to the earlier cash till that the cash register replaced. July, 1886. p. 86. **Lower Middle: Kruse Check and Adding Machine Co. "dial" register.** One of the first serious competitors to NCR and the first broadly marketed total-adding mechanism that cumulated all cash transaction values during a day into a grand total. ca. 1887. p. 106.

The Vestal Press, Ltd.
Vestal, New York 13851-0097

© 1988 Richard L. Crandall

Library of Congress Cataloging-in-Publication Data

Crandall, Richard L., 1943-
  The incorruptible cashier.

Bibliography: v. 1, p.
    Includes index.
    Contents: v. 1. The formation of an industry, 1876-1890
    1. Cash register industry—United States—History. 2.
Cash registers—Collectors and collecting—United States.
3. Cash registers—United States—Catalogs. I Robins, Sam,
1947-   . II. Title.
HD9801.6.C383U 1988   338.4'768114'0973   88-135
  ISBN 0-911572-69-4 (v. 1)
  ISBN 0-911572-70-8 (v. 1. : pbk.)

Contents

Foreword
by Sam Robins

Cash register collecting is a relatively new corner on the hobby scene compared with some collecting mainstays such as stamps, coins, cars, etc. One question frequently asked is, "why would people want to collect registers?" There are a number of reasons.

First and foremost, most of us start out by being attracted to the beautiful and intricate brass cabinets. When polished, a brass register looks like a giant jewel, almost a shrine to the money it was made to hold. It's hard to visualize that a mechanism that is so commonplace today was a real novelty when first introduced and needed handsome and elegant cabinets to be accepted. Today's store owner wouldn't consider being without a cash register, but upon introduction, just the idea and function alone was not enough. Early cash register manufacturers had to sell their products not just by merit, but also as a fixture every store owner would be proud to own and display in his establishment.

That same original lure is the one that captures the interest of the collector today. Whether a collector has just one or 300 specimens, he or she usually has an appreciation of what went into making the early models.

Another factor to consider is that the early cash registers represent the know-how and evolution of the American inventor when the mechanized age was beginning to gain full momentum. Interchangeable parts, assembly line production and planned sales approaches were found not only in the auto industry, but were also found in and some were initiated by the production of cash registers.

As a collector progresses, he or she begins to admire the subtle differences in development from one early year to the next. The Ritty and other early entrants were quite primitive compared to models made just ten years later, although some employed total adder technology that was a dozen years ahead of their time. The advanced collector considers these as the most desirable and valuable. Some collectors have a broad range of machines trying to represent just about every model and maker. The problem of both space and pocket book generally prevents most of us going that route.

I found that some collectors acquire only NCR machines, all others being considered "offbrands." Frequently many collectors just keep a certain style of NCR. For example, a collector might have just wood cabinet models or narrow candy store type machines. Other collectors are fascinated by the variety of design found in the "offbrands." What makes this such an interesting hobby is the diversity found within the realm of cash registers.

One point pretty much agreed upon is that most of the collections stop at the end of the brass era around 1917 or so. The remaining cash register manufacturers could no longer produce the ornate cabinets due to a metal shortage during World War I and had to convert to a plainer, more functional model. Unfortunately, the new appearance was the modern look of the time; the "old brassy" never returned.

One aspect of antiquing is that the item you collect has to be somewhat difficult to obtain, but not so difficult that you can't build up a collection. Any collector delights in telling the story behind finding a particular machine, perhaps even enjoying the search more than the ownership.

Now what do you do with the machine once

you obtain it? You're faced with a few choices here. When first starting, most collectors tend to just accumulate cash registers, whatever may be available at the right place or price. Perhaps someday in the future many of these will need to be weeded out and sold, leaving the keepers that will likely be restored. After a while certain machines usually seem to be sought after to fill in a gap or just because you're attracted to one model or another.

A big question is whether to restore or not. Frequently, this is a project from which many people get enjoyment that is equivalent to the hunt. The beauty of a brass register is realized when it is completely polished and redone looking like it did the day it left the factory. Sure, there are some pristine original examples that perhaps should be kept that way, but for the most part, machines generally have a higher value when restored.

Each collecting area seems to have its own rules regarding restoration. For example, a coin collector would shudder at the idea of polishing up a rare coin, but how many prize-winning automobiles have you seen with original paint and chrome? Many machines were painted every time the owner redecorated his shop, so you're not hurting originality by stripping and restoring it properly. How far and to what degree a machine should be restored is best left to the individual collector. If a machine is to be fully restored, it should approximate the original. Over-restoring would alter the basic function or original appearance of a machine and would certainly hurt its value.

For as long as I can remember I've been a collector: stamps, coins, butterflies, you name it. My dad still thinks that during my college years I majored in collecting beer tap knobs. These were the knobs that screwed on to the draft beer faucets with the individual name and logo of each brand. I amassed what was then the largest collection in the country. In my efforts to display the collection, I wanted an old time saloon environment.

Along with a bar itself, I felt one of the most important pieces was an ornate old brass cash register. I bought my first one from the dad of a woman with whom I used to teach. He was in the used shoe equipment business and was happy to sell it to me for $20.00. Part of the intrigue of collecting to me was the history, the restoring and finding out what makes an item tick. The same night I bought the register, I had it all torn down, stripped the paint from the brass cabinet and then polished the metal.

In the process of trying to locate missing parts and keys, I discovered the multitude of styles and sizes of these old registers. Each one was unique in its own way. The collector in me took over. As with any other hobby in its early stages, you think you're the only nut out there collecting registers. Through the grapevine, I became aware of other collectors and I began contacting them and vice versa. We reinforced each other's habit, having only each other to rely on for parts and information.

Cash register collecting has certainly become a recognizable world-wide hobby with collectors as far away as Japan, Paris and London. Parts and information in the early days were basically nonexistent. Out of necessity, I began to manufacture parts for the restoration of my own machines. Today, I'm one of the fortunate individuals that has been able to turn a hobby into a full-time business dealing in registers, their parts and restoration. The parts dilemma was solved, but not so with reliable information. We sorely needed a reference guide in the form of a book.

I first met Rick Crandall in 1979 when a mutual friend brought him over to see my collection. Rick had been collecting in other fields, specifically early mechanical music devices. It was only a matter of time before the cash register bug would bite. Rick spotted a Chicago Cash Register I had, and the wheels started turning. He had to have one. A Chicago was finally located out in California, and I arranged for Rick to buy it. Since then, Rick has given up resisting collecting in yet another area. Now, six or so registers later, I think he's hooked.

Rick had previously published and researched information on early mechanical music devices and with his skill and willingness to write, research and photograph, it seemed natural for us to embark on this project. I feel this book has combined both my years of practical knowledge and Rick's diligent research of background and history. Writing has never been one of my favorite activities. Rick took on the tremendous task and has now provided the collector with an important guide and the non-collector some interesting reading with an insight into American ingenuity and technology just prior to and after the turn of the century.

It is hoped that this book will generate new interest in the cash register collecting field and will serve to provide more frequent new discoveries. Careful thought and editing has gone into the writing and photography of this book. It has been our goal to provide information as correctly as possible.

To the best of our knowledge, everything contained in these volumes is correct, but the reader should keep in mind there are very few rules in the register field and there are many exceptions.

Sam Robins
c/o Play It Again Sam, Inc.
5343 W. Devon
Chicago, IL 60646
(312) 763-1771

Preface

There has been little definitive writing on the subject of antique cash registers other than a few articles and some NCR-sponsored texts on its founding president, John F. Patterson. When Sam Robins told me that, it was like waving a red cape in front of a bull.

Sam Robins of Chicago, Illinois, has been one of the primary collectors, restorers and dealers in the field; he has been the most prolific source of technical and model-availability information. On the other hand, while I've been an avid collector, my own interest and experience has been oriented to research, history and a more complete understanding of the motives and personalities responsible for the early development of the cash register. So, we joined together, and in spite of a number of obstacles that came up in the process, we produced this book.

Anyone who has read texts on 19th-century mechanical inventions may have already recognized that there is good coverage of the telephone, the phonograph and even the typewriter. The cash register is always excluded, undoubtedly for the lack of available information. Here, the cash register will take its proper place beside the surprising list of important inventions that all appeared at the same time in the 1870's.

Perhaps it all began in the 1860's when the gear, the cam and the spring combined with early assembly-line procedures to make mechanical manufacturing feasible. There is no question that by the 1870's, something sparked in America. Inventiveness exploded upon the scene. Consider the following:

1873	Christopher Sholes invented the first American typewriter.
March 10, 1876	Alexander Graham Bell was first heard distinctly through the telephone: "Mr. Watson, please come here, I want you."
August 12, 1877	Thomas Alva Edison sketched the first commercial phonograph.
1879	George Seldon of Rochester, New York applied for the first patent of a gasoline powered motor carriage.
December 31, 1879	The New York Herald devoted a page to Edison's wonderful and novel electric light—although still in the experimental stage.

In that same decade, patents were issued for the first cash registers. By 1879/1880, James Ritty had his Incorruptible Cashier on the market.

Why is it that so much invention occurred in such a short span of time? Part of the answer lies in the mastery of the new technologies of mechanics, acoustics and electricity. Another factor was the prolific inventiveness of the "Wizard of Menlo Park," Thomas Edison. He captured the American creative spirit and set a pace that others could but exhaust themselves in attempts to keep up.

Yet another factor was the new-found protection afforded by the U.S. Patent Office. Inventions could be protected in the 1870's, not so in the 1850's.

It takes a number of forces coming together at once to create an environment for new inventions. The United States is going through just such a period now in the 1980's. Fueled by the miniature integrated circuit (new technology) and the availability of venture capital financing (funding), the pace of current inventiveness is breathtaking. There are many parallels between the 1880's and the 1980's.

Surely a book like this ought to exist: collectors need a reliable source of information and historians need a reference book on the cash register, the most important predecessor of our modern business machines.

This first volume is mainly historical in nature. It covers the 1876-1890 period of first invention and early development of the cash register. From a collector's viewpoint, registers shown in this volume are rare and, therefore, difficult to find. There are perhaps 100 examples extant of all models (NCR and independents) highlighted in this volume. Of course, more may be discovered. Usually when published books first become available in an antique field, collector interest is heightened and new and exciting discoveries are made. Perhaps the same will occur with early cash registers so that they may be saved from obscurity or destruction.

The research for this work has been difficult. The main obstacle was NCR's intransigence by not allowing access to their substantial files on early machines. NCR's reluctance to share its information was contrasted with every other such pioneering company I know of who are generally most willing and even anxious to share their files with historically minded individuals. Usually, the problem is that no records were retained. We did get written permission from NCR to use literature of theirs that we located on the antique market.

So, we dug and scrounged for four years. Gradually, we assembled NCR catalogs, advertising brochures, promotional material and some materials on the independent competitors. Then a big break came: I had known about the U.S. Government's Antitrust lawsuit against NCR in 1911, and finally I located the government agency that had saved the paperwork—all two thousand one hundred pages of testimony by the presidents of the important cash register competitors, as well as that from executives from NCR. Unraveling that much documentation took time, but there was much meat in it to fill out the bare bones of catalog material we had assembled earlier.

Another important source has been the diligent job Sam has done in absorbing and recalling facts about extant machines—their features, their rarity and their present owners. Several other collectors and dealers gave some assistance, although not very many compared with similar endeavors in other areas.

Dan Lewis has been a real supporter of this effort. He had photos, original material and machines generously loaned for this effort.

Thanks are given to Jimmy Filler of Birmingham, Alabama, who helped by letting me photograph his collection *twice*. The first time the photo processor went broke and was closed down by the New York State tax office. Harvey Roehl, president of the Vestal Press, jumped into the fray and retrieved some important photos, but others had to be retaken. Well, no one said it was going to be easy!

Many thanks to Dick Bueschel, author of many books on coin-operated collectibles, who dug through his files several times to contribute valuable historical information.

Other materials were contributed by Al Levinson, an avid cash register collector. Marshall Fey, descendant of Charles Fey, the inventor of the three-reel gambling machine, contributed some materials relevant to cash registers he had come upon in producing his book on slot machines. Also thanks to Bob Gilson, Q. David Bowers, Bob Feldman, Bob Strauss, Henry Bartsch and Tom Kunkel for their assistance.

Bill Gunn of Comshare undertook the task of photo processing the thousands of photos from which the 650 were selected for inclusion in these volumes. Rachael Gardner, my secretary, fed the reams of written material into her trusty word processor and even maintained her customary cheeriness through countless drafts. Peter Heydon, an accomplished English scholar and collector-enthusiast, gave this book a careful reading and offered many useful modifications to the writing. The people at Vestal Press, in particular Grace Houghton, helped with further editing of the text for greater readability, and Pat Peck of Comshare produced the artwork for the Early Cash Register Chronology shown at the beginning of this volume.

The Smithsonian Institution aided not only by cataloging and providing available photos, but also by piecing together early literature from several boxes in the Warshaw Collection of Business Americana, which was made available for this effort.

Finally, thanks to my five-year-old son, Brett, whose irregular sleeping habits, inherited no doubt from his dad, wakened me at odd hours of the night with nothing else to do but work on these volumes.

There will soon be a second volume published covering the "brass era" of cash regis-ters from 1890 to 1915. It will include some more history and hundreds more photographs, plus a complete field guide to cash register identification.

This effort is far from finished. Now that this first edition is done and our efforts to produce a definitive work has credibility, I hope that those of you who have a machine or literature that should be added will contact either Sam or me so that future editions might progress.

Rick Crandall
P.O. Box 1588
Ann Arbor, Michigan   48106

Photo Credit

Most of the photographs in this volume were taken by Rick Crandall. Where other sources were used and the source is known, credit is given in the captions. The workhorse camera was a Nikon F3 with 55mm micro-Nikkor lens and Kodak Pantomic-X (ASA 32) black and white film. Development and printing was done mostly by Bill Gunn of Comshare. Most of the catalogs were supplied by Sam Robins, whose quest for original literature was invaluable for this effort.

Part One

The History

The Cash Register—A Place in History

We're not so clever. It has taken us more than 100 years to implement the business automation that originally was made possible by the invention of the cash register in the 1870's. Still today in many retail establishments, bells ring, drawers pop open, indicators jump up with amounts paid and counters record cumulative transactions.

You can find all these functions on the NCR Model 35 of 1892, nearly 100 years ago.

Finally a change occurred during the 1980's: the "telecommunications networked optical scanning electronic point-of-sale terminal," a fancy way of describing the new "register" showing up in supermarkets and other high-volume retail stores. Such devices will finally antiquate their predecessor cash registers.

The transition has been far easier than in the 1880's when a hoard of entrepreneurs sprang up around the country, each with his own gimmick to help the store owner reduce pilferage from the open cash drawer.

The first cash registers were heavily promoted as theft deterrents to be sure. But they were also instruments of a new analytical approach to business which resulted in a systematized use of information to produce profits. There were accounting and executive information features in the turn-of-the-century cash register that do not exist in many machines today. How many company executives today know daily sales and cash received? But now the register is becoming part of a broader business system. They are now considered sources of input data and have moved into the realm of data processing, "decision support" and executive information systems.

In 1902, you could get an audit trail of transactions, a customer count, detailed amounts rung and cumulative totals. You could get all of this for each of several sales clerks. You could even identify individual product transactions. This permitted special sales promotions, individual clerk-incentive schemes and the collection of quantitative market research data.

The cash register was a combination of a security system, accounting machine and a management information system. All this was implemented with moving mechanical parts, gears, cams and levers and housed in grand cases. If that wasn't enough function, the cash register also expanded beyond its namesake (the handling of cash) to the extension of credit. Its special credit function keys helped the store owner keep tabs on amounts due and amounts paid.

Thus, the cash register was the mechanizing force behind the profitable use of information about cash and credit. Ironically, the electronic cash management systems of today will eliminate cash with its automatic connections to bank accounts. This will truly make the cash register 100% obsolete, marking the intensification of an important collectable field.

Indeed, we need to preserve early examples of the cash register. One hundred years from now, cash will be a distant memory, and the collector's cash register will be the most fitting tangible monument to what will then seem the curious use of printed money.

Overview

The chart entitled *Early Cash Register Chronology* presents a concise view of the various styles and principles of the National Cash Register Company, as well as particularly noteworthy competitors, including their lifespans and the

A National Cash Register assists clerks in serving customers quickly.

nature of their destinies.

Of course, there were hundreds of companies and thousands of models, but many of these were brief attempts at cashing in on the birth of a new industry and never amounted to anything. Hallwood was the most notable exception. It was clearly number two in the industry with a broad line of attractive and well-built registers. But make no mistake, Hallwood was a distant second to National, the latter firm having established a 90% market share as early as the 1890's.

The Michigan Cash Register Company was a latecomer, but only under the security blanket of an auto company parent did it survive and produce significant quantities. The city of Detroit was a hotbed of cash register manufacturing, particularly extremely inexpensive

machines distributed to wholesalers of goods who in turn gave the cash registers away as free premiums to induce bulk purchases. They became known as "premium" machines and some, such as Osborn, Weiler and Detroit, achieved relatively high volumes of sales.

NCR's legal assault on its competitors are legendary, some of which are recounted herein. The Boston company was the unfortunate recipient of the first blast of NCR's legal cannon. Boston lost its defense and became the first bankruptcy casualty of this type.

Ideal and Chicago are noteworthy for the sheer beauty of their case designs. Ideal's products also drove NCR to manufacture a brand new register, the 171-principle lever-operated machine which was kept in the product line for five years after NCR acquired

A National Cash Register stops mistakes and carelessness at your fountain.

Ideal. Then there were the Bensinger, Boston, Kruse and the Hopkins & Robinson registers which were all early contemporaries with NCR's start-up. Each was innovative and unique in its own right.

Bensingers are almost unknown today, but they and their inventor played a crucial role in the industry. It was NCR's acquisition of Bensinger's inventor, Thomas Carney, that provided the technology for the 35 and the 79 principle—the basis for National's two major successful total-adder product lines during the entire brass era.

The Simplex and the Sun stand out for their unusual mechanization of the ancient abacus adding principle. Kruse and Boston each have a special place in the formation of the industry and in the collecting world. They were the first

to popularize the total adder when National was still promoting its detail adders which were primitive by comparison. A Boston or Kruse dial are rare to be sure, but they are possible to find and acquire for the determined collector.

It was Kruse's dial register that National dressed up with a cherub and moon casting after acquiring Kruse. In either form, the result is one of the handsomest combinations of metal, wood and mirror formatted in a simple esthetic clock-like dial pattern.

Within the National line, there are seemingly an infinite number of styles, models, finishes and technologies to study and/or collect. All the pre-1888 machines were encased in wood. The Ritty and National Manufacturing machines are extremely rare and highly collectible for their historical importance. They were the vehicles used to start the industry in the 1879-1884 period.

The early NCR wooden deep-drawer machines, the first produced under the NCR name, sported some of the most beautiful inlaid wooden furniture cabinets ever to encase a mechanism. These, too, are very rare (perhaps 30 known), but at least feasible to acquire.

After 1887 the brass era commenced, and one case design outdid the other. The designs used on the machines intended for top-of-the-line status at NCR became classics. Some of these were custom designed by Tiffany Jewelers of New York. One such design was the "Dolphin" case, which adorns the classic cash register of all time, the NCR 313 brass candy-store machine. When properly buffed and restored, the 313 is a veritable jewel. It is desired by many, even many non-collectors, and fortunately there seems to be an inexhaustible supply. Surely, thousands of 313's exist today.

Towards the end of the brass era, some of the larger NCR machines were laden with features: multiple drawers, clocks, counters and the like. For the technology buff, happiness is a Model 592-EL which is crammed with impressive mechanical features, but good luck restoring one with serious problems. Fortunately, Nationals were built to last and most unabused examples will work with minor cleaning and caring. Of course, as values increase, full restorations are becoming more popular.

A Machine Is Born

James Ritty of Dayton, Ohio is generally credited with inventing the cash register in 1878. Our research indicates that while there were cash register inventions patented before the Ritty register, none appeared to have succeeded commercially. Unless some new revelation is uncovered in the future, it can be said that James Ritty, before the National Cash Register Company was established, invented a device and received associated patents that led to early domination of an industry that later broadened into the massive computer and office equipment industry of today.

As is the case with most attempts to ascertain who was the first at anything, the cash register picture is unclear. For example, the Cash Recording Machine Company of New York City had its cash recording machine on the market (at least in ads) in early 1878 for a price of $75.

A comparison of these early registers will reveal the following differences:

	Cash Recorder	Ritty Machine
Amount Indicators	No	Yes
Receipt Printer	Yes	No
Printed Audit Trail	Yes	No
Cash Drawer	No	No
Keys	Yes	Yes
Adder	Yes	Yes
Invention Date	1876	1878

Clearly, these registers each "registered" money purchases and were early cash registers. To date, the Cash Recording Machine is the earliest identified device of its kind, but that too could change. Indeed, the Ritty brothers themselves state in their 1879 patent:

> We are aware that it is not new in registers to use recording discs, dials, bells or keys; and consequently, we make no claim to the application of such independent devices to a register.[1]

The Rittys claimed, with patent office concurrence, the "first use" of an individual transaction indicator (initially the dial and subsequently, the more traditional pop-up indicators), *plus* a cumulative adder (later called a "total adder"). Even when the same key was depressed multiple times, the indicator stayed in the same position, but the adder incremented its total appropriately. Without question, it was the Ritty patents that were upheld many times in court actions as the fundamental patents documenting the original state of the art of the industry and which gave rise to NCR's eventual dominance.

Of course, if one loosens the definition of cash register to "any device which can record money transactions and cumulate them," we presumably need to go all the way back to the abacus which is estimated to have been in use in China thousands of years B.C.

THE CASH RECORDING MACHINE
Affords an absolute check on Receipts and Payments of Money. It is fully described on the first page of this paper. Price $75 each; but in order to test its completeness and applicability to every business, it can be rented for $4 per month for not less than six months. The rent ($24) may be applied during that period on the purchase if full title is desired. Address
CASH RECORDING MACHINE CO.,
P. O. Box 737, N. Y. city, or 148 Worth St., New York, and 21 Sycamore St., Buffalo, N. Y.

Fig. 2-1: Ad in February 16, 1878, *Scientific American* for the Cash Recording Machine invented by John Moss of New York City and John Smith of Buffalo.

Today you can still find the abacus in use in some Chinese retail establishments—an amazing product with a life span of some 4500 years. The abacus is easy to learn, can store a result (if no one upsets the beads) and can even be used as a "total adder" to cumulate transaction values during the course of a day. It is interesting to inspect the Simplex and Sun registers which mechanically implement many of the strengths of the abacus.

A Frenchman by the name of Charles Xavier Thomas reportedly produced the world's first commercially successful calculating machine in 1820. It performed the four classic arithmetical functions of addition, subtraction, multiplication and division; despite its features, neither it nor any derivative from it ever saw use as a money recorder for business.

The Cash Till

It is difficult to imagine a retail store without a cash register; yet before 1879, merchants had no such equipment. Few actually knew if they were operating at a profit or a loss. While store owners may have gone to great lengths to instruct clerks to record all sales transactions in a "Day Book," rarely was this consistently done. Negligence, illiteracy, laziness and dishonesty made proper accounting an impossibility.

Temptations to pocket money were overwhelming since cash was usually in open cash boxes or even in clerks' pockets as a normal matter of course. The proprietor could not determine whether he was suffering pilferage since he had no accurate account of actual cash taken in, the number of transactions or which items sold.

Retail store owners found themselves living on cash flow produced from inventory liquidated at sales prices which could not support continued operations. The only way a firm's financial condition could be determined was by taking physical inventory, a time-consuming and arduous procedure not often done.

The most significant pre-register attempt to put cash under lock and key with a bell annunciator was the "cash till." This was simply a cash drawer, usually mounted under the counter, with a push button opener. The bell's ringing told the proprietor to glance over at the till because it was being opened.

The principal maker and patentee of the alarm cash till was the Miles Alarm Till Manufacturing Co. and its successors. Founded in 1859 and incorporated in 1869, Miles was located at 500 South Main Street, Providence, Rhode Island. The Miles Alarm Till had a sliding coin drawer of a type that was later copied by the National Manufacturing Company and NCR in their "deep drawer" registers of 1883-1887.

Another firm, W. H. Tucker & Co., was formed in 1865 on 197 South Meridian Street, Indianapolis, Indiana. Their first till was called "Tucker's Pat. Combination Alarm Till Lock and Cash Drawer." The Tucker sold for $5 retail in 1870. This firm evolved into the Tucker & Dorsey Co. by 1877.

By early 1878, the Miles firm merged with Tucker & Dorsey. Their combined patents became an effective barrier preventing others from entering the competitive scene.

William Tucker and Robert Dorsey won one of several important legal battles against Samuel and Erastus Frink on February 15, 1877. Tucker & Dorsey leveraged their 1870 patent #5566 (which claimed novelty of its lock catch plate) to block continued manufacture of the Frinks' device which had been sold under the name of Frink Alarm Till Mfg. Co. The Frinks were driven into insolvency.

The victors in these wars had a clear playing field. It would be a full decade later, in the 1880's, that NCR would dominate the market with its full cash register line. Tucker & Dorsey never became a factor in the cash register market; Miles may have had a brief go at it since there is a Miles register produced in Boston, although it is not clear these were the same firms.

Conception of the Cash Register

There are a number of stories of how the idea of a cash register came into being. They all stem from similar concerns.

Fig. 2-2: NCR replica of original Ritty patent dial register.

A *Scientific American* article on "The Cash Recording Machine" bills the invention as

. . . a new machine for making people honest—a consummation to which (if it ever can be attained by machinery) no small amount of inventive genius is just now being brought to bear.

Hitherto most efforts have been directed to the mechanical shoring up of the consciences of car conductors and stage drivers; but the present inventors have advanced higher, and propose to apply the same salutary influence to the moral sense of every class of employee within whose duties the handling and disbursing of cash is included.

It must have occurred to any one who has noticed the Babel of confusion which exists in any large city retail drygoods store, for example, when crowded with shoppers, and when a constant stream of cash boys circulates between clerks and cashiers, that scarcely any system of checks and records depending upon the memory and fidelity of the employee can exist which does not leave loopholes for fraud. We are not prepared to assert that the present machine will at once substitute a system in which it is impossible to swindle, because it is a lamentable fact that there is perhaps nearly as much ingenuity enlisted in the service of sin as in that of virtue, and somebody

may discover how to "beat" even the most thoughtfully contrived mechanism; but the new "cash recorder" certainly offers a very simple mode of keeping forcibly accurate records and, for our part, we fail to see where the chance to defraud it exists.[2]

The certainty of these statements about infallibility arises from the ingenious idea of involving the customer in the audit process. In the words of the patent,

This is accomplished by registering on a paper strip inside the machine the amount of any transaction, and printing or stamping the same amount simultaneously upon the account, bill or ticket inserted for that purpose.[3]

By printing the transaction amount on a check receipt for the customer, inaccuracies would become highly visible. By printing the same amount on an inaccessible audit tape locked within the machine, the proprietor could add the numbers on the audit tape at the end of the day and compare them with the contents of the cash box. The store keeper might further motivate a customer audit by posting a money-back reward to anyone not receiving a correct receipt, a practice occasionally seen even today. Shortages in cash thus clearly became the clerk's responsibility.

The machine is equally applicable to the disbursements of money. The article about the Cash Recording Machine concludes

It is small, strong and compact, measuring a little over a foot in length, by four inches wide and less than a foot high. It is placed upon a glass stand which acts as a receptacle for the paper upon which each transaction can be seen as it is charged against the operator.

Apparently after very slight practice the figures can be manipulated with a rapidity equal to that accomplished by the use of a pen, while the receipt, date and signature are completed much quicker than by hand.[4]

The problem of pilferage was indeed pervasive. It is not surprising that more than one store owner would have been worrying about the impact on profits.

Established 1859.

Incorporated 1869.

Miles Alarm Till Mf'g Co.,

400 to 406 South Main St.

Providence, R.I., October 16" 1878

S. N. BROWN, JR., Pres.
A. O. MILES, Treas.

Hon A. G. Murphey

Phil^a Pa

Pizen Man of the City of
Brotherly Love

Sr Sir Knight Gr Ro

Your Telegram just received — No Mice or Rats

You will recollect that when I was in your city ~ "or dont you" that I said we would send "Schegler" a "Coffin" Well we want his Photo to put under the "Slap" We are now waiting for it — In your letter — you mentioned that S. had sent one by a friend — Have not seen it Now I do not ask you to go 40 Milz — or over frozen ground — But you would do me a favor if you can send me one — Old Boy there will Come a day of "Reconing" and you will be there Talk about "Hay" Sr Hooper will want to and "have to" take some of his "Pizen" if he or you ever show your face in these "Plantation" again

Fraternally Yours

A. O. Miles

Fig. 2-3: Courtesy Smithsonian Institution.

Established 1859.   CAPITAL $25,000 00.   Incorporated 1869.

OFFICE OF

Miles Alarm Till Mf'g Co.,

400 to 406 South Main Street,

Providence, R. I., Feb. 1st, 1878

TRADE MARK.

A CARD TO THE TRADE.

Gents:

In 1859 the "Miles Alarm Till Mf'g Co." was Established and in 1869 was Incorporated under the laws of Rhode Island, and in 1866 the Firm of Tucker & Dorsey was established for the manufacture and sale of "Alarm Money Drawers," and since that time there has been Granted and Assigned them several Patents, bearing dates as follows, viz: July 5th, 1859, June 6th, 1866, March 7th, 1867, March 16th, 1869, May 17th, 1870, Sept. 9th, 1871, June 17th, 1873, Sept. 19th, 1873 and Dec. 23d, 1873.

The above Patents cover nearly all the essential points in Alarm Till Locks. These Patents have been sustained by the United States Courts in several closely contested cases by parties who were infringing in the manufacture and sale of "Alarm Money Drawers," and an Injunction has been granted, in every case, against the parties. And we are now prosecuting others who are now making and selling "Alarm Money Drawers," which we believe to be direct infringment upon some of the above Patents. And we shall not only hold manufacturers but dealers responsible for such goods, wherever sold.

All of our Patents bear the stamp of the "Miles Alarm Till Mf'g Co., or Tucker & Dorsey upon the top of the drawers. And all dealers selling our goods, with the above stamp upon them, will be protected by us.

We have not issued this as a Threat but as a Friendly Warning to the trade. But we mean just what we say.

Thanking the trade for their many favors in the past, we hope by prompt and strict attention, to merit a continuance of the same, and remain,

Yours Very Truly,

MILES ALARM TILL MF'G CO.
TUCKER & DORSEY.

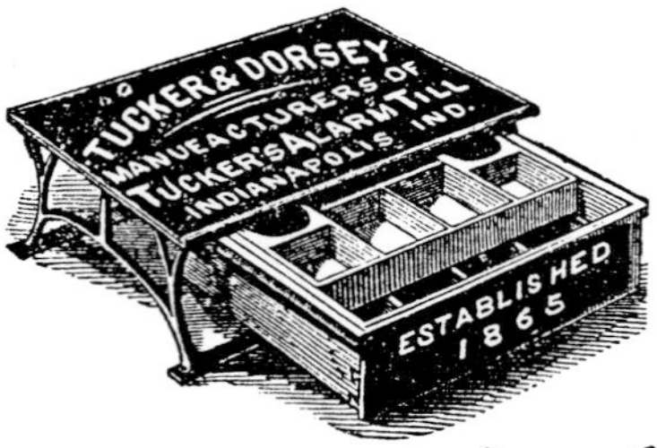

Office of **TUCKER & DORSEY,**

MANUFACTURERS OF

TUCKER'S ALARM MONEY DRAWER

No. 15 Bates Block,

Indianapolis, Decr 18th 1877

Messrs Riehle Bros

Gentlemen

we make you net prices — If you want
cheaper goods we can send you # 2 or
Best Tumbler goods at 20cc —

We cant regulate the selling price —
we retail ourselves at 4.00 #1, 3.50 #2
we sell a great many goods at 3 to 6cc
you only advance on these prices
billed, as you to the small trade —
Some jobbers offer our goods in small quantities lower than we will sell — we
dont amt to the price after goods leave
us — You ought to make a large retail
trade in connection with your Sales —

We have advice from Russell Power
that they shipped you the Second
crate — will you be kind enough to ad
vise us if the second crate has
been received — Yrs 28 25

Tucker Dorsey

We send you a duplicate invoice —
dont let them get mixed up —
You are now charged with 1 Dozen
Altogether

Fig. 2-4: The Cash Recording Machine of 1878.

James Ritty

Another inventive spirit with similar concerns was James Ritty, a saloon owner in Dayton, Ohio. Ritty's business was booming in 1878, but there were no profits. Ritty came to despair about suspicions that his bartenders had their hands in the till. So, to relieve his tensions, he booked a vacation steamer trip to Europe.

The story goes that Ritty, having been trained originally as a mechanic, became interested in the machinery of the ship. He paid particular attention to the counting mechanism that recorded the revolutions of the ship's propeller shaft. With thoughts still fixed on the losses in his saloon, he had an inspiration: why couldn't a store's sales be recorded in mechanical fashion similar to the ship's propeller revolutions?

The inspiration proved an instant cure to his personal distress; he even booked immediate return passage from Europe without staying there a single day! Back in Dayton, Ritty excitedly confided his idea to his brother John, a skilled mechanic. Together they began work on their own home-grown original version of a cash register.

Inventing things on the spur of the moment

was a common practice of the period. It was 1878, one year within an extraordinary decade of great mechanical invention.

In what would later be seen as a fateful omen for a much later confrontation, a now-famous inventor named Hollerith was in 1886 trying out punched cards with tablulating machines in the Baltimore, Maryland Department of Health. His effort would later evolve into the IBM Corporation. All of these "can-do" technical inventions seem to have derived from high expectation about the limitless future coupled with a rapidly growing understanding of mechanics. Add to these an environment of no government regulation, labor unions or other barriers to productivity and the result is the vast array of mechanical predecessors to nearly all of today's electronic marvels.

When the Ritty brothers invented their cash register, they did so within the same tradition of many of the other inventors of the day. Rather than pursuing some long-range plan based on clearly focused goals, they responded to a clearly defined problem with a quick prototype. When the prototype showed faults, they added to the invention to fix the problem.

The Rittys' first model had two rows of keys across the lower front of the machine with denominations of 5¢, 10¢, etc., to $1.00. When pressed, each key recorded a specific sum of money. Sales amounts were shown on a dial face with two hands similar to a clock's (possibly reminiscent of the ship's revolution counter that had suggested the idea in the first place). One hand indicated dollars and the other cents.

They had found an adding mechanism patented by McNary in May, 1870. It may have been the same adder which had been used on the ship since both were affixed to a revolving shaft to count revolutions. The Ritty register employed a shaft turned by key presses: the keys engaged an arm connected to the shaft causing a specific amount of rotation corresponding to the value of each key. The adding wheels had numerals in sequence imprinted on them so that the total transactions for the day processed through the register were recorded for the shopkeeper to compare with actual cash accumulated at the end of the business day.

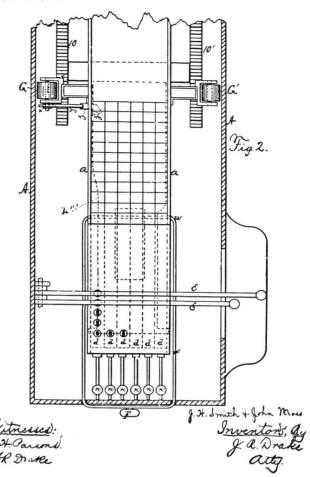

3 Sheets—Sheet 2.

J. H. SMITH & J. MOSS.
DEVICES FOR PRINTING AND RECORDING CASH RECEIPTS.
No. 188,310.   Patented March

Fig 2.

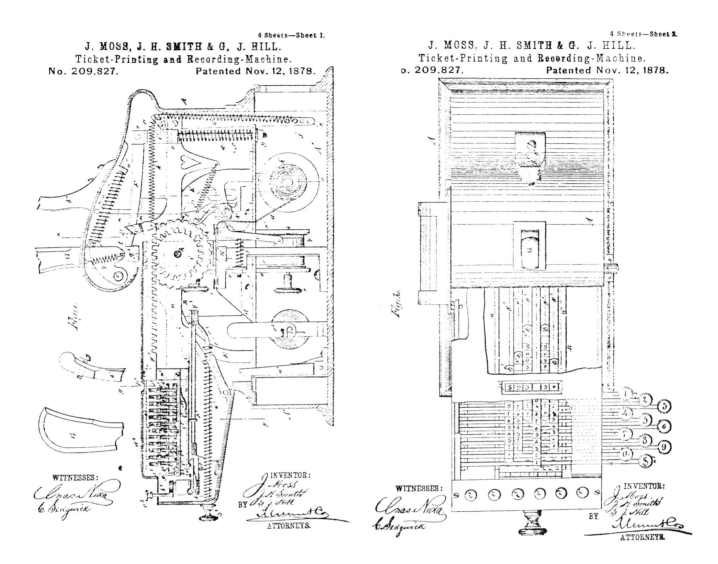

4 Sheets—Sheet 1.
J. MOSS, J. H. SMITH & G. J. HILL.
Ticket-Printing and Recording-Machine.
No. 209,827.   Patented Nov. 12, 1878.

4 Sheets—Sheet 2.
J. MOSS, J. H. SMITH & G. J. HILL.
Ticket-Printing and Recording-Machine.
o. 209,827.   Patented Nov. 12, 1878.

WITNESSES:

INVENTOR:

BY

ATTORNEYS.

Fig. 2-5: Drawings from two patents for the Cash Recording Machine. The first was filed on October 25, 1876, and was assigned to Erastus Wiman; the second was assigned to the Cash Recording Machine Co. of New York City: "This invention is to provide a machine for the purpose of keeping an exact record of all cash transactions . . . in stores . . . or any business establishment where monies are paid in. It is also intended to be a check on employees and a prevention of dishonesty by clerks . . ."

The "dial" machine was the basis for the first Ritty patent (#221,360) awarded on November 4, 1879.

The patent for the machine describes a bell to "ring up" sales in audible fashion, whereby both the customer and anyone else listening knew that the sale had actually been recorded by the register. It also had a total adder that summed all the cash values of the key presses during a day. The clerk couldn't pocket money during the day for fear of its being missed at the end of the day by comparing cash and the register's total adder. While it is doubtful that this first machine ever found its way into the commercial market, there is no literature uncovered to date to explain why it didn't.

Perhaps the use of a clock-type pointer on a dial face was not sufficiently legible to accomplish the purpose of displaying the sale. Even at NCR, there are no examples of this dial register despite the practice of keeping one of almost every important model since the beginning of the industry. Decades later, NCR produced a number of replicas of the dial machine, one of which was given to the Smithsonian Institution, while others remain at NCR. These "replicas" can be easily spotted since their dial faces show the numbers running in a direction opposite to that pictured in the patent drawings.

While Ritty had solved the adder problem in 1879, the previously mentioned Hollerith worked all through the late 1880's finally incorporating a decimal total adder into a tabulating machine in 1891. While thought to be innovative, it was 12 years after the Ritty invention and five years after Kruse's entry into the field.

Fig. 2-6: James Ritty.

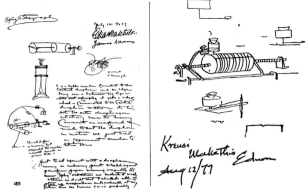

(Left) EDISON'S ORIGINAL SKETCH OF THE PHONOGRAPH.

Reproduction of page of Edison's note-book in which he recorded his first conception of the phonograph.

(Right) EDISON'S FIRST WORKING DRAWING OF THE PHONOGRAPH.

Reproduction of Edison's sketch of the first phonograph with instructions to Kruesi, his modeller, to "make this."

Fig. 2-7a.

REPLICA OF SELDEN CAR (1877).

This car was built to demonstrate the operativeness of the Selden automobile in a patent-infringement suit.

Fig. 2-7b.

By courtesy of Munn & Company. From the Scientific American of March 31, 1877.

INTRODUCING THE TELEPHONE TO THE PUBLIC.

The public had to be taught the principle and function of the telephone. Hence Gardner Hubbard, Bell's father-in-law, arranged a series of lectures to be given by Bell and Watson. The first demonstration was given before the Essex Institute of Salem, in 1877. Watson, in Boston, played musical instruments and sang. The audience was delighted.

Fig. 2-7c.

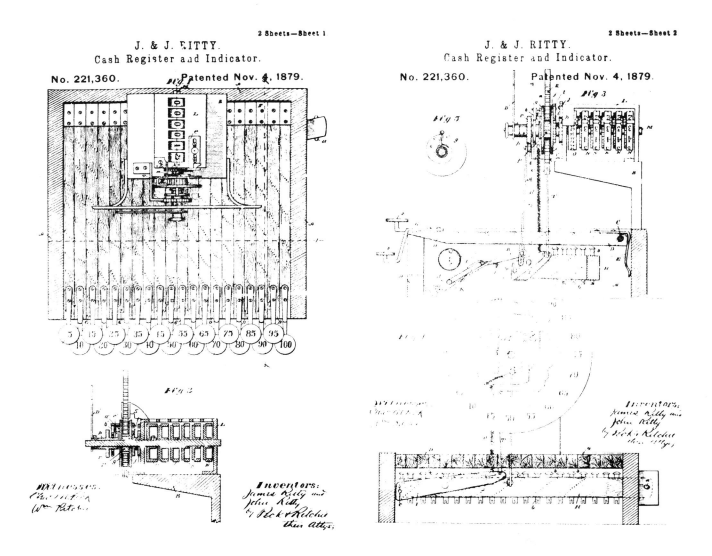

Fig. 2-8a, b: First Ritty brothers patent filed March 26, 1879.

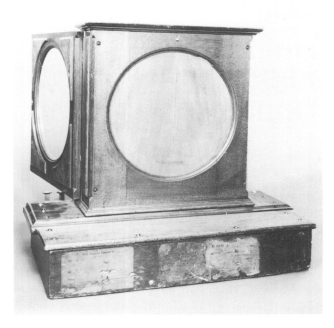

Fig. 2-9, 10, and 11: First Ritty dial machine. Note clockwise direction of denominations. These are contrary to the counter clockwise direction of the patent drawings. This is one of the three or four machines NCR made in the 1940's. They have no mechanisms. Courtesy, Smithsonian Institution.

[3]

Ritty's "Incorruptible Cashier"

Ritty's Incorruptible Cashier was in many ways the real beginning of the cash register business. It was the first product of the first incarnation of the National Cash Register Co., (the name the Ritty Brothers chose to call their fledgling enterprise). The Incorruptible Cashier differed from the Ritty dial in that for the first time, pop-up indicator tabs were used. These were metal tabs with denominations pressed into them that corresponded to the key values. The tabs were mounted on stems and aligned in a row vertically positioned so that when a key was depressed, the corresponding tab popped up into a glass window on top of the register to display the amount just keyed. Such a display method was to become the standard in the industry.

The Incorruptible Cashier preserved the total adder described in the first patent. Although this historic register had push-down keys and a bell, it had no cash drawer. Presumably it was intended as simply the added security needed to make an existing under-counter cash till more workable.

There are no known records of how many of Ritty's Incorruptible Cashiers were produced, but the number must have been small.

The Incorruptible Cashier depicted in Figure 3-3 is a rare survivor. We are fortunate that at least this example has survived (there is another later one at NCR). It has the number 18 stamped in the case.

A close examination reveals a machine that was clearly hand made. The case is professionally constructed (perhaps by Ohmer, a Dayton firm mentioned in Chapter 7) with some detailing; it is painted. Some effort obviously has been expended in case design even at that early time of scant income. It is finished in black lacquer with gold and green pinstriping.

Centered on the upper crest is an unusual cameo depicting a hand-painted mountain and cloud scene. There might be some symbolism suggested by the cameo, but what that is we don't know presently. The model tag is attractively designed as seen in Figure 3-1.

There are two rows of 10 keys each. Depression of a key causes the corresponding indicator to pop up and the appropriate key value added to the cumulative total adder. The adder is located on the right side and must be viewed from that side. While such positioning was relatively inconvenient by comparison to the central location under the front lid that Nationals carried in the future, it must be remembered that the proprietor had only to view the total once a day.

There is a bell. The indicators can be viewed from the front only, since the register would be pushed against a wall.

This machine is complete and fully functional. The key checks are nickel-plated

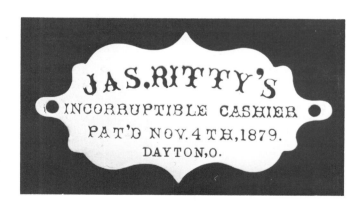

Fig. 3-1: Model identification tag from the Incorruptible Cashier.

Fig. 3-2: The first cash register factory. The photo shows a Ritty dial and an Incorruptible Cashier and more being made. This was the state of things around 1881.

silver and the indicator tabs are nickel plated brass. Both have hand-stamped impressed numerals filled with black paint. Overall, the Incorruptible Cashier is not only the first incarnation of a workable cash register technology, but it sports a certain charisma owing to its unique design, its height, its stylistic touches and its primitive, but functional, total adder. It is also shrouded in mystery—Why the mountain scene? Why was the total adder abandoned in the next incarnation, only to return in 1892?

In a curious step backward, the successor Ritty machine abandoned the initial total adder mechanism in favor of a very different registering mechanism which employed a pair of counter wheels to measure dollars and cents for each key. This feature is called "the detail adder." In the words of the patent:

To keep a register of the machine, all the wheels are first set with their zeroes just in front of the brakes at the commencement of the day's work, and each key keeps an independent register of the number of its operations, so that at the end of the day's work the proprietor, on opening the case, can read off the wheels the totals of their operation. For instance, the five-cent key may show a register of $12.50 on its two wheels, the ten-cent key will show a register of $20.40 . . . and so on, the readings being taken from the numbers exposed just in front of the brakes.

He jots down these different sums and adds them up, and so ascertains exactly the amount of cash that should be in the till.[1]

The detail adder represented less convenience for the user. It was undoubtedly simpler to build and service since each key had its counter

Fig. 3-3: The Incorruptible Cashier (circa 1879-1880). This is a 20-key total adder with key values from 5¢ to $1.00 indicating its probable use in a saloon. The number 18 is stamped in the case. Rick Crandall collection.

and did not have to interlink with other counters. This detail adder had inherently less friction, and hence required less finger power, particularly at times when arithmetic "carries" were occurring on the total adder. The detail adder became the technology for Ritty's successor machines all through the 1880's.

Some confusion still exists between the patent chronology and the recollections found in several biographical works written in the 1920's and 1940's about NCR's founding president, John Patterson. Ritty produced a primitive printer version of what was to become a "detail adder." The individual keystroke count was accomplished not by wheels, but by punched holes in a paper roll with a ratchet advance

Fig. 3-4a: The Incorruptible Cashier, right-side view with adder cover removed.

amount would be displayed clearly for all to see and would be recorded reliably on the machine's counters for a later audit check by the shopkeeper.

This patent was the basis for several of NCR's later attacks on competitors for patent infringement. Its earliest action, lasting for years, was against The Boston Cash Indicator and Recorder Company. The initial decision was adverse to the Ritty & Birch patent. In the Opinion of the Federal District Court, Boston, on March 23, 1891,

At the date of the Ritty and Birch invention, it was admitted that cash registers were old:

A series of keys, rods and indicating tablets are to be found in the prior English Pottin patent of

Fig. 3-4b: The Incorruptible Cashier, left-side view

feature in the register. Each key had a pin on it that would prick the paper when the key was depressed. At any time, the shopkeeper could count the pin pricks for each key, multiply them by the key value, and then sum across all keys to get the grand total registered.

This paper roll machine reportedly preceded the counter-wheel detail adder. However, patents show the detail adder was invented in 1882 and the paper roll machine came along in 1883. Whatever the sequence, both machines were a real backwards step from the total adder; but they were surely more reliable and simple to keep in adjustment. The patent for the indicator detail self-adder model was filed on February 15, 1882 and granted in January of 1883 (#271,363) to James Ritty and John Birch, also of Dayton. The stated purpose of the machine in the patent was to insure that when a sale was made, the

Fig. 3-5a: The Incorruptible Cashier close-up, rear view of mechanism with indicators removed. Note the bell towards the right. The adder is a shaft counter.

Fig. 3-5b: The Incorruptible Cashier, close-up of key mechanism and part of adder outside of case. The top adder wheel adds to $5 and the bottom wheel increments every $5 to $500.

Fig. 3-6: Ritty and Birch detail adder patent of 1883 used so often to thwart other cash register start-ups.

Fig. 3-7: Ritty and Birch detail-adder patent of 1883.

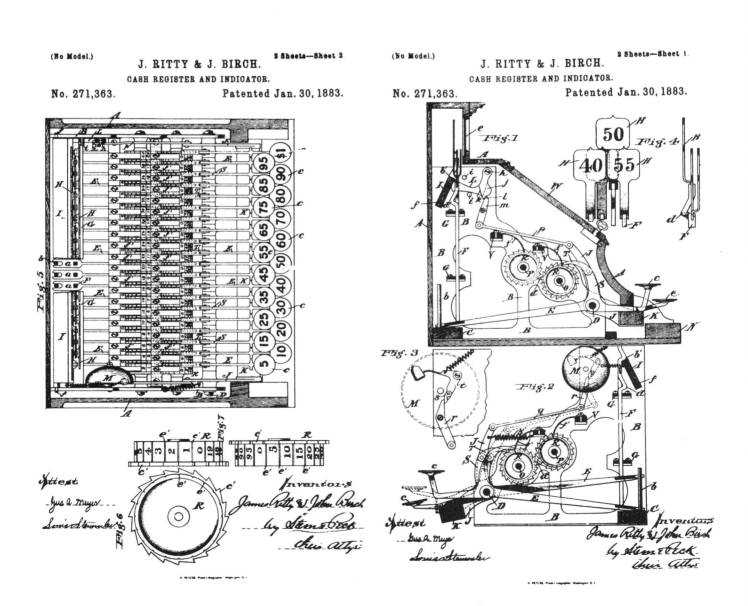

May 28, 1877, and in the Campbell patent of February 14, 1882. In these machines we find an indicating mechanism which in its general features is the same as that of the patent in suit. The most therefore that Ritty and Birch can claim, in view of the prior state of the art, is an improvement upon the Pottin and Campbell registers, and that improvement consisted in devices whereby it was made certain that the preceding tablet would fall when another tablet came into view.[2]

The initial decision against NCR in this case was carried to the United States Supreme Court (No. 155 October Term, 1894) who reversed the initial decision in favor of NCR.

To sum up the state of the art, then, at the date of the Ritty and Birch patent: The use of keys to raise vertical rods carrying tablets was not only well known, but lies at the foundation of every cash register to which our attention has been called. It was also old to use a pivoted wing or bar to catch a projection or elbow of the vertical rod for the purpose of holding the tablet exposed to view, until another tablet was raised. So, too, the use of a sliding bar actuated in one direction by a spring and in the other by a projection from the vertical rod or its tablet, was a recognized equivalent of the pivoted wing. And, finally, a connecting mechanism operated by each one of the keys by means of a bar over or underneath them had been previously used for ringing the bell, opening the cash drawer, and in other machines for other purposes.

What then was the contribution of this patent to the art? It was found that not only must the machine be constructed with extreme and almost impossible accuracy in order to operate as desired, relying on the shoulders alone to move the wing, but that, when the machine was put to use, some of the keys would be used much oftener than others, and the shoulders on the tablet rods belonging to these keys would become worn so that, when one of these keys was operated immediately after one that was less frequently used, the shoulder on its rod would not move the wing back far enough to release the tablet rod of the infrequently used key, which was resting on the wing. So, too, any accumulation of dust, dirt or oil upon the projections or bar would render their operation uncertain. The consequence was that two tablets might be in view of the customer at the same time. This not only failed to indicate to the customer the amount of his purchase, but afforded to the salesman an opportunity of deceiving the proprietor as to the actual amount of his sales.

Indeed, it requires no expert to see that where all the rods are constructed alike, and the fall of one rod is made to depend exclusively upon the elevation of another, the mechanism would soon become so worn as to be inoperative. To obviate this, Ritty and Birch subdivided the power exerted by the keys in the operation of the pivoted wing, and caused such wing to be put in motion not only by the elbow of the rod, but by the simultaneous, though wholly independent, action of a bell-crank lever, which receives its impulse from the bar beneath the keys, and, with its other arm, shoves back the upper side of the wing far enough to permit the tablet to fall and resume its original position in time to suffer the wing to fall back and catch the elbow of the last tablet rod, and hold it up. . . .

It did however require thought to conceive the idea (1) that a remedy for the existing defects in the machine lay in the independent operation of the wing; and (2) that such operation could be secured by a mechanical connection with the keys.[3]

Ritty's invention thus won the day, making his register the clear progenitor of all advances that were to come in business automation. NCR also managed to buy the Campbell patent (#253,506 dated February 14, 1882) for a royalty of $.50 per machine incorporating the cash drawer and opener features present in the Campbell patent.

Formation of the National Cash Register Co.

During the earliest days of the Rittys' activity, the rather ambitious name of National Cash Register Company was chosen for the somewhat un- assuming familial partnership. The business offices consisted of a single room over James Ritty's saloon at 10 South Main Street in Dayton. By 1881, however, the Rittys had moved to a factory building in which at times they employed as many as ten men making wooden machines (see Figure 3-2).

James Ritty kept running his saloon. As he compared the problems of pioneering a cash register industry with running his now profit- able saloon, he opted for the saloon. Research indicates that up to 1882, only 19 machines had been sold; of these, John Patterson (later of NCR fame, but then a small businessman in Coalton, Ohio), bought four.[1] It is doubtful that so low a production figure is accurate since one extant Ritty machine carries serial number 514. It is possible that the serials started at some number higher than zero or one, but six Rittys are known still to exist which would be highly improbable if only 19 were originally produced.

In late October, 1881, the business was sold to Mr. Jacob C. Eckert for $1000. Eckert brought in his brother-in-law, John Birch, as a machinist who would later work with Ritty to develop the register further. The Birch and Ritty patent for the indicator detail-adder register, when issued in January of 1883, was promptly assigned to Eckert who financed production of the machine. Eckert changed the name of the company to the National Manufacturing Company and succeeded in obtaining additional shareholders.

It was actually John Birch who engineered the locking cash drawer in August of 1884 (patent #303,974) which went beyond the Campbell patent and became a basic component of cash register design owing to its vastly improved security. Sometime during the same period of 1883-84, a version of the earlier Ritty punched- paper register was also produced. The technol- ogy for the early years was firmly focused on the detail-adder mechanism, and the total adder did not reappear in the National line until 1892.

Some marketing benefits were thought up to justify the otherwise clumsy system. While it was true that performing the summations manually would get the same result as the total adder, the detail adder's extra detailed reporting allowed the store owner to run product promo- tions on products priced with a unique key value. For instance, if a product were singled out to be priced at 15¢, the store owner could count the sales of the product separately from all other transactions. Ritty filed for a patent on the printer model in September 1883, but a patent was not issued until May of 1885.

A good explanation of Ritty's thinking on the subject of paper punch technology is found right in the patent:

> . . . the keys are numbered in the progressive series 5, 10, 15, up to 55. The paper has printed upon it at intervals, in rows coincident to the keys, numbers to correspond with the respective keys. . . . The perforations, then, made by each key will be in a straight line along the paper, as shown.
>
> At the end of a day's work, or whenever it is desired to ascertain how much has been regis- tered, the proprietor, who alone has access to the cabinet or case in which the machine is confined, with his hand turns the roller . . . until he brings all of the perforations between the cutting bar . . . and the roller . . . and with a knife, and the bar has a guide, severs the paper.
>
> He then lifts out the roller . . . detaches there- from the perforated paper, and proceeds to count the perforations in each row. For instance, we will

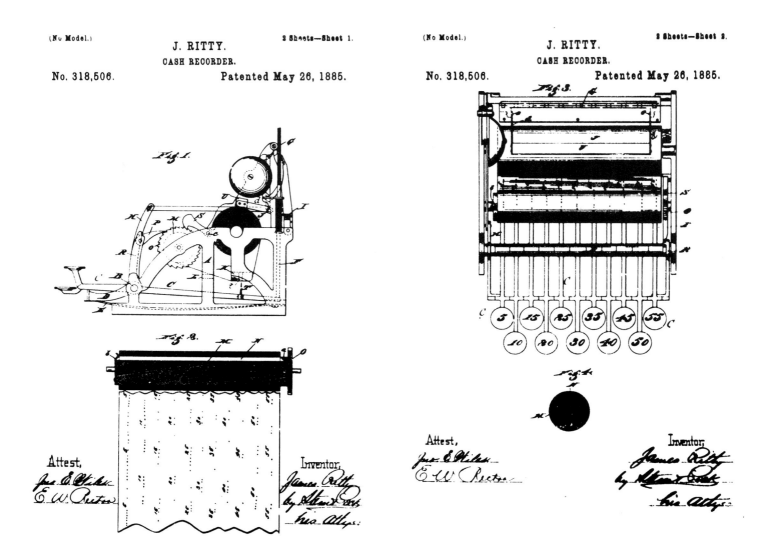

Fig. 4-1: Ritty paper punch patent of 1885.

Fig. 4-2: Ritter paper punch patent of 1885.

suppose he finds seventy in the five-cent row. He jots down $3.50 and proceeds to count the next or ten-cent row . . . until he has counted all the perforations, and by adding the different sums ascertains how much cash has been taken in. He then, to reset the machine for the next day's work, draws forward the cut end of the paper from the roll . . . replaces the roll . . . in its journals, and engages the end of the paper with the bar. . . . He is then ready to start the machine again.[2]

Ritty assigned his patent to the National Manufacturing Company which must have been

a misnomer since by then ownership had changed hands again and the name was also changed — back to the National Cash Register Company.

The way this developed is that when Eckert went to find equity investors, one of the new financial partners was John Patterson. He originally became an investor in May, 1883, as a 25-share owner (par value $50 each) out of a total of 300 shares outstanding. It didn't take long for Patterson to become a member of the Board of Directors and then scretary of the corporation.

He had previously established himself as a businessman in a grocery and general store in Coalton, Ohio, which sold goods to miners. In an undated NCR flyer, John Patterson himself tells the story:

> We were obliged to be away from the store most of the time so we employed a superintendent. At the end of three years, although we had sold annually about $50,000 worth of goods, on which there was a large margin, we found ourselves worse off than nothing. We were in debt, and we could not account for it, because we lost nothing by bad debt and no goods had been stolen.
>
> But one day I found several bread tickets lying around loose, and discovered that our oldest clerk was favoring his friends by selling below the regular prices. Another day I noticed a certain credit customer buying groceries. At night, on looking over the blotter, I found that the clerk had forgotten to make any entry of it. This set me to thinking that the goods might often go out of the store in this way without our ever getting a cent for them.
>
> We made an investigation and found that these errors were going on right along, and we concluded that there must be many more which we never found out.
>
> One day we received a circular from some one in Dayton, Ohio, advertising a machine which recorded money and sales in retail stores. The price was $100. We telegraphed for two of them, and when we saw them we were astonished at the cost. They were made mostly of wood, had no cash drawer, and were very crude [Ritty's Incorruptible Cashier]. But we put them in the store, and, in spite of their deficiencies, at the end of twelve months we cleared $6,000.
>
> The order and system ENFORCED by these machines had enabled us to secure for ourselves all the money coming to us from the sale of our goods. I said to my partners: "what is a good thing for this little store is a good thing for every retail store in the world. When this machine is properly constructed there'll be an enormous sale for it."
>
> As soon as we could get a little money together, we bought an interest in the concern that was making these machines and pushed the business as hard as possible. Wherever we introduced the register, the mistakes it corrected and the amount of money it saved for the users amazed us.
>
> But the machine was then a mere crude, undeveloped idea—no more like a modern cash register than a birch-bark canoe is like an ocean "liner." We worked hard, employed skillful mechanics, and invented and added hundreds of improvements to these machines, until finally, after overcoming almost insurmountable difficulties, were able to put on the market perfectly constructed cash registers adapted to every business.[3]

During the few short years that the National Manufacturing Company was in business from the end of 1881 to the end of 1884, various models of the detail adder were produced. Model numbering of National Manufacturing machines followed a very simple pattern:

Model 1	:	11-key detail adder		(1¢)
1½	:	11-key	" "	(5¢)
2	:	20- or 25-"	"	(1¢)
2½	:	20- or 25-"	"	(5¢)
3	:	30-key	" "	(1¢)
3½	:	30-key	" "	(5¢)

It is likely that other specialty machines were made, including some continuing production of the paper-punch machine. The practice was to make each machine almost as an individual item. Certainly it is a fact that there are no two cases alike on the extant National Manufacturing machines, although they were all wood: walnut, cherry or mahogany.

Between 800 and 1000 machines were made during the short life of the National Manufacturing Company, most of them being the large format models, 2 1/2 and 3 1/2 "saloon" registers. They were so called because their key values started at 5¢ for drinks rather than the 1¢ denomination needed for retail establishments. Purchase prices ranged from $50 to $200.

After much hesitation, John Patterson talked himself into buying control of the National Manufacturing Company when the opportunity arose in December, 1884. The purchase price of $6,500 seemed so high that all who knew about the sale laughed at the price. But Patterson hit the business like a whirlwind. He renamed it The National Cash Register Company in December, 1884, bought out the remaining minority shareholders (NCR remained a family-owned company until Patterson's death in 1922), and introduced modern selling methods to get the business going.

At first, the road was tough. Although in an age of mechanical invention, the populace was in the habit of passing off new ideas as fads. The cash register had an especially tough reception because pilfering clerks were solidly against its introduction. To combat such resistance, Patterson built a national sales force, the first to use a professional selling cycle and sales pitch. Such techniques are still very much in use today amongst most large professional sales forces, particularly in the computer and office equipment industry.

Patterson continued with the National detail adders as his sole products, although he did do some renumbering of the models. Earlier National Manufacturing machines that came

A Confession.

I am the oldest criminal in history
I have acted in my present capacity for many thousands of years.
I have been trusted with millions of dollars.
I have lost a great deal of this money.
I have constantly held temptatio₂ before those who have come in contact with me.
I have placed a burden upon the strong, and broken down the weak.
I have caused the downfall of many honest and ambitious young people.
I have ruined many business men who deserved success.
I have betrayed the trust of those who have depended upon me.
I am a thing of the past, a dead issue.
I am a failure.

I am the Open Cash Drawer.

Fig.4-3: Patterson's message remained the same from 1885 through 1915 (when this page was published) and beyond. His was a personal as well as a corporate crusade against the open cash drawer—justifiably so.

back to the factory were reconditioned and re-tagged as NCR products. One extant machine appears to be an early NCR model 1, but it looked too primitive to its present owner; underneath the NCR model tag, he discovered a National Manufacturing tag identifying it as a Model 1 1/2.

In the year 1886, sales increased to 1050 registers, up from 500 the year before. This brought the total number in operation at that time to approximately 2500. Sales accelerated throughout the rest of that decade reaching a shipment rate of 10,000 machines per year by the end of 1890. NCR was on its way to total domination of the industry.

A fortune was spent on advertising and direct mail to educate the public and to establish National's name as a well-known entity. An ad which appeared in *The American Store Keeper* of Chicago in August of 1886, said:

What is a Cash Register?:
It is an automatic cashier which records mechanically every sale made in a store. It never tires. It never does one thing while thinking of another, and never makes a mistake. It is a mathematical prodigy in brass and steel, all of whose computations are infallably correct. It is a machine which will save the money you make and thus pay for itself over and over again.[4]

[5]

A Blizzard of Competitors

Ritty, and subsequently Patterson, were not the only people who saw the cash register as an opportunity. In fact, in the last two decades of the 19th century, there was a frenzy of entrepreneurial and competitive activity. An industry was in formation, lawsuits and all.

Between 1888 and the mid-1890's alone, 84 companies were organized in the United States to produce cash registers. The NCR trade-in guide for 1915 listed over 350 companies, and all must have had at least some machines on the market, although many companies did not last very long at all. There were less than two dozen firms that put up any kind of competitive fight. It was NCR's strategy to use every means of legal protection and every competitive technique to weaken the competition or to put them out of business altogether. Many businesses were acquired. NCR historians contend that the acquisitions were foisted upon them by shady entrepreneurs formed to infringe on NCR's inventions as nuisances, so NCR would buy them out to get them off the market. While some of this kind of activity was no doubt going on, there is also no doubt that acquisition and legal suits were mere arrows in Patterson's quiver of techniques to achieve domination.

Frederick Fuller of Union

A non-NCR perspective is given by one competitor, the Union Cash Register Company of Waterbury, Connecticut. Frederick Fuller, the chief inventor of the Union Cash Register, wrote a book later in life after he had occupied several prestigious positions including chief inventor of NCR itself, succeeding the famous Charles Kettering. The Union Cash Register Company was certainly formed for real business reasons based on real innovations receiving real U.S. Patents. It apparently sold thousands of machines and was acquired by NCR in 1907.

Union's products and staff must have represented something much more than a "nuisance" as is evidenced by the promotion of Mr. Fuller to a position of chief inventor in NCR.

It was the Union Cash Register in 1892 that won the John Scott Legacy Medal presented by the City of Philadelphia based on the recommendation of the Franklin Institute.

Fuller gave his perspective on the NCR acquisition:

> It was inevitable that this should happen, and that the National should decide to buy the Union. Our cash register was too good to be allowed to compete, and it had a number of features that the National felt it should have in its own machines. . . .[1]
>
> My original assignment at Dayton was to finish the model of a cash register on which I had been working for the Union in Trenton, before it was purchased by the National Cash. This model I completed and Patent No. 1,117,179 was the result. . . . When I took charge of Invention Department No. 4, my principal task was the development of the No. 1200 line. This was the line that later was known as the No. 2000.[2]

This picture of the benefits accruing to NCR from the acquisition of the Union is completely different from the general NCR perspective on the subject of acquisitions as presented by Isaac Marcossen, the personal friend of John Patterson who became NCR historian. In his book, *Wherever Men Trade*, published in 1945, Marcossen talks about the inevitability of the "storm of court contests" over imitations and patent infringements. He states:

The original National cash registers were crude and cumbersome. Their expanding success was achieved through a multitude of improvements. These improvements were not conjured out of the air. They were the result of years of investigation and the expenditure of millions of dollars.[3]

In 1927, T.J. Watson, once NCR vice president of sales and, subsequently, president of IBM, hired Fuller from NCR to be an inventor for IBM. In the preface to Fuller's book, Watson said:

> Every generation produces a certain number of individuals whose fortunate lot it is to contribute to the general good of mankind. . . . My friend Frederick Fuller is a member of that select company of men upon whom Providence has conferred inquiring minds and the additional boon of practicality. . . . His practical mind has helped him patent nearly a hundred inventions which have been incorporated into machines which bring peace of mind through elimination of drudgery. . . . I am very glad to have had a part in making it possible for others to get a glimpse at the human side of a truly great inventor.[4]

There is more evidence that NCR did not exactly corner the market on innovation.

Bensinger and Cuckoo

No mention is made of the beneficial involvement in the NCR line from staff and machines acquired from others. Indeed, later in his book where he discusses the NCR 35-principle registers, (the most successful early technology NCR ever used), Marcossen admits that the 35-principle total adder came from the acquisition of Bensinger in 1891.

Marcossen continues:

> The concentration of so many improvements in one line of registers and the reduction of manufacturing costs through the use of specially designed and patented machinery, soon enabled the NCR to offer and publish widely its Great Guaranty "To provide a better cash register at a lower price than any other company." Unable to meet this sweeping challenge many competitors resorted to a campaign of abuse of NCR, its officers, agents and product. They attempted to enlist public sympathy by posing as struggling concerns crushed by a "vicious octopus."[5]

An amusing example of NCR's efficient use of patent protection is actually offered by Marcossen:

> In 1894 a Detroit cafe owner, Michael Heintz by name, organized the Heintz Cash Register Co. . . . started to make a register called "Cuckoo" which was sold for $85. Instead of ringing a bell with each operation of the machine a bird would emerge from an arrangement similar to that on a cuckoo clock and make a sound resembling "cuckoo." The NCR filed suit against Heintz in August 1895 for infringement of the Campbell cash drawer patent and secured a permanent injunction which silenced the cuckoo. An accounting for profits and damages was waived because Heintz had manufactured and sold only a few machines.[6]

Whoever was the more aggressive, NCR or its competitors, one fact is certain: the 1880's and 1890's were a period of bitter fighting. Every manner of legal and competitive tactic was used, many of which would not hold up under any reasonable standard of ethics, but such was the nature of competition during that day.

Premium Registers

Some companies chose to compete head-on with National and others looked for unique niches. Somewhere around 1891 the unfilled need for really cheap registers was filled by the Seymour made in Detroit. Then cheap detail adders exploded on the scene as a way to price under National's line. These detail adders were priced in the $15-$45 area, but they were most often offered free as a premium by the wholesalers of the very goods the registers would ring up at retail. For example, cigar distributors would buy quantities of these premium registers and give them away along with the sale of cartons of cigars to cigar stores who would use the registers for as long as they worked.

Competing against premiums was difficult for NCR since the registers appeared to be free. The first premium register manufacturers were the

THAT YOU MUST HAVE A CASH REGISTER

in your store is no longer a question. The only question is: Will you buy one and pay a fabulous price for it, or will you send us your order and get one absolutely without cost to you? Which of the two propositions sounds best to you?

The Merit Cash Register is the most simple machine ever built. Has fewer parts than any machine of its capacity. Up to date in every respect. Built to last a business lifetime. We guarantee these registers for three years, and will send a written guarantee with each machine.

THE MERIT CIGAR CO.,
79 Park Place, DETROIT, MICH.

OUR GUARANTEE Detach, sign and return Order Blank, and we will send you on ten days' trial one Merit Cash Register and 1000 of Four Choice Brands of Cigars—250 of each brand, to be returned at our expense if you do not consider Cash Register and Cigars as represented and entirely satisfactory.

CUT OFF HERE

State if you prefer denominations from 1 cent to $10 or 5 cents to $20.

THE MERIT CIGAR CO.,   2-13- No. T.
79 Park Place, DETROIT. MICH.

Ship via Freight as soon as possible, F. O. B. Detroit, subject to approval:

1000 CIGARS, FOUR BRANDS, 250 OF EACH,   -   - $44.50

ONE MERIT CASH REGISTER FREE.

If I am not pleased with the goods I will return them within 10 days from date received, otherwise I will remit for same.

Terms—2% discount for cash in 10 days, or 30 days net.
Denominations 1 cent to $10 or 5 cents to $20.

Name..

Town..................................

Date.................   State........................

We give a Special 5% Cash Discount if paid upon receipt and examination of goods.

FREE GIVEN AWAY FREE

THE MERIT CIGAR CO.

Will GIVE AWAY Without COST TO YOU

THIS LATEST IMPROVED

DETAILED ADDER CASH REGISTER

IT'S THE WORLD'S LEADER

UNEQUALED IN UTILITY, ACCURACY AND WORKMANSHIP

TO INTRODUCE OUR FOUR CHOICE BRANDS OF CIGARS, WE WILL GIVE AWAY, FREE OF COST, THESE RELIABLE MERIT CASH REGISTERS

Fig. 5-1a, b: Typical promotion for a premium register. Note that $44.50 buys 1,000 cigars, plus a "free" register. These cigars retailed for 5¢ and undoubtedly wholesaled for 2 1/2 cents. The Merit was really a Peninsular (of Detroit, Michigan) Model 41 nickel-plated 25-key register that retailed for $40 and probably wholesaled at $20. So, 1,000 cigars equals $25 plus $20 for the register adds to a wholesale total of $45, which was being "introduced" for $44.50. The register was not free at all!

Seymour and the Weiler, both founded in Detroit. Entrepreneurial job-hopping seemed to be the primary reason for others also forming in Detroit and that city became the Mecca of the cheap register. For example, William McGraw, founder of the Seymour, sold that concern in 1894 and proceeded to form the Detroit Cash Register Co., followed by the Globe Cash Register Company and finally the Century Cash Register Company, all in Detroit.

It was these premium registers that motivated NCR to keep its inexpensive detail adders in the product line long after they had any functional justification for being there. Except for the Century, a cheap total adder, all the Detroit premium machines were detail adders. They were much more flimsily built than the National machines.

Eventually, NCR found ways to sue all of the makers of premium registers. As a final blow, Patterson authorized the purchase of the Weiler Cash Register Co. in Detroit with an idea to compete secretly with the premium register companies without using the National name. The enterprise was short lived since Patterson could not be satisfied with the production of a low-quality machine. A number of competitive stories are available in Marcossen's book, but these are suspect for their bias towards the National version of the truth.

Ideal

Whether commissioned by NCR or whether of his own volition, Marcossen used substantial bias in his attempt at rewriting history. A graphic example of substantial and repetitive inaccuracies can be found in Marcossen's description of the NCR battle with the Ideal Cash Register Co.:

> Between that year [1888] and the mid-nineties, 84 companies were organized in the United States to produce cash registers. The great majority followed an identical pattern. They were started primarily to force NCR into buying them out because of their nuisance value. . . .
> A . . . pretentious premium register enterprise was launched by the Ideal Cash Register Co. incorporated September 30, 1897 at Bound Brook, New Jersey, and capitalized at $1,000,000. . . .
>
> The campaign of the Ideal Cash Register Company was so typical of the methods employed against NCR. . . . The Ideal Company did put out a register with a detail strip and a check printer at an increased price. . . . Business slumped. The factory was closed down in 1903. In April 1904 the corporation went into the hands of a receiver.[7]

Characterizing Ideal as an example of how companies competed with NCR would tend to disprove his whole theory that there was unfairness on the part of National's competitors. However, Ideal was not in business to get purchased by NCR. When Ideal's Dr. R. V. Pierce resisted National's acquisition attempts, National's general manager, Hugh Chalmers, went to Buffalo with several cash registers in tow. He brought an Ideal and an example of NCR's 171-principle machines that had been specially used to knock the Ideal competition. Patterson himself had authorized Chalmers to spend as much as $125,000 in acquiring Ideal—not exactly petty cash for eliminating a "nuisance."

Marcossen's claim that Ideal's business slumped to the point of going into receivership in 1904 was completely wrong, a curious error for the company historian. NCR records surely include the papers from the 1911 U.S. Anti-Trust suit against NCR, even if the original records have been destroyed. These records clearly document that NCR acquired Ideal according to a carefully constructed game plan.

Chalmers recalls:

> Before the purchase was made we were usually pretty active against them [Ideal] in the field, trying to replace the machines. We became more active after we decided to purchase their plant.[8]

As far as the Ideal being a cheap premium machine, that too appears to be controvertible by the evidence. Certainly the solid-bronze Grecian-Art-cased total-adder Ideal that sold for $100-$125 was no premium machine. Most premium machines were detail adders with a retail price of $15-$45. Cheaper pot-metal-cased Ideals may have been used as premium machines, but the NCR sales force looked upon the Ideals as direct competition.

Marcossen's inaccuracies are not surprising given his orientation. His book has a clear public relations objective rather than a serious historical objective.

Boston

One of NCR's earliest uses of legal means to oppose a competitor was against the Boston Cash Indicator and Recorder Co. founded in 1886. In October of 1888, NCR sued Boston for patent infringement and five years later, the suit was dismissed with the Circuit Court decision in favor of Boston. Patterson was persistent. He escalated the battle to the Supreme Court of the United States. There the decision was overturned in October of 1894 and Boston was out of business by the end of 1895.

If ever there was a jump-off point in NCR's quest for total domination, surely the Supreme Court decision must have been it. With the Supreme Court behind it, NCR blitzed its competitors with lawsuits for the ensuing 20 years.

Hallwood and American

Probably the biggest court drama involving an NCR competitor was with the Hallwood Cash Register Company.

Henry S. Hallwood purchased the Sern P. Watt patents on a cash register that was powered by pushing in the cash drawer at the end of a transaction rather than using finger power on the keys. He organized the Hallwood Cash Register Company in 1892. As soon as Hallwood began developing a real market share, the competitive scene became quite hot, particularly with NCR.

Today, these methods would come up against the law and the regulatory agencies. They are so blatant that they are almost comical, but at the time, they helped destroy companies which had no staying power. Hallwood was one of the companies which had staying power for a while and was vocal to boot. Its catalogs were replete with references to alleged NCR practices. Here are some excerpts:

It [the old Hallwood model] is a good register, and it has met with phenomenal success, in spite of the depraved methods of competition used by the NCR Co.

We are sorry to allude to them, but feel compelled to do so, to preserve our business lines and in order that the public may appreciate the value of fair competition.

. . . they have been gnashing their teeth, in impotent rage, and spending their substance in crushing and buying out thousands of Hallwood old model registers at a fabulous cost to themselves . . . [9]

Grand old Phillips Brooks once said that he never inquired "How much wealth a man left, but asked, what character has he left."

The N. C. R. character is found on this and the following page.

CIRCULAR LETTER.

THE NATIONAL CASH REGISTER COMPANY,
DAYTON, OHIO, U. S. A., February 4, 1892.

TO ALL MANAGERS:

We send you under separate cover devices for beating the Simplex Cash Register which consists of a lead bullet with a common horse hair attached. We want you to have your agents call on the parties who are using the Simplex Register, in your territory, and explain how easy it is to beat them. (But do not show them how to do it.) You can easily ask the proprietor to step away about twenty feet from the machine, and then by concealing the bullet in your hand register any amount you wish by simply dropping the bullet in the small hole directly under the amount you wish to register.

In all cases be sure and withdraw the bullet from the machine at the same time that you open the cash drawer (that is providing you can get the combination of the lock), which can easily be done.

Of course, if you do not want to open the cash drawer you can step away from the machine and the proprietor (*unless he has an eagle eye*) cannot discover the horse hair protruding from the machine. Be particularly careful to cut the horse hair off so that it will protrude only about one inch from the opening.

We think agents will have little trouble in using the above simple device effectively and impressing users that they have a machine which can easily be beaten and is worthless.

Kindly let us know what success you have in using the above device.

OPPOSITION DEPARTMENT, THE N. C. REGISTER CO.

Fig. 5-2: Hallwood catalog reprint of an 1892 NCR letter describing the so-called "Bullet and Horsehair Technique."

A $200 Hallwood for $80.00   A $150 Hallwood for $60.00
A $175 Hallwood for $70.00   A $135 Hallwood for $54.00

Store-Room at Our Dayton Factory

This room contains 2,185 Hallwood registers. About 500 more are in our agents' hands

ANY HALLWOOD CASH REGISTER IN OUR   In Other Words, 40 Cents on the Dollar
POSSESSION WILL BE SOLD ON TERMS GIVEN BELOW

We sell these registers on easy monthly payments, or allow you 5 per cent. discount for cash

Fig. 5-3: NCR mailer, undated.

A Word to the Timid:

Past circumstances seem to warrant us in saying just a word relative to patents. It is a notorious fact that a certain Cash Register concern claims to control patents covering about every principle mortal man has ever thought of in connection with machines for registering cash, and often in the past this same concern has tried to intimidate prospective buyers of Sun Registers. Believing fully that the merits of the New Sun No. 10, which we are now putting out, will cause the aforesaid concern to rant more than ever, we will, at the risk of being premature, state a few facts:

First.—The principle embodied in the "Sun" Registers is absolutely clear of all patents except our own.

Second.—There is not the shadow of a chance that any suit will ever be brought by any responsible person against the manufacturers, buyers, sellers or users of "Sun" Registers. This was tried once—about three years ago—and the Acting U. S. Judge, Southern District of Ohio, literally kicked the case out of court.

Third.—We broadly agree to protect all who buy, sell or use "Sun" Registers in any matters of infringement.

Fourth.—The very fact that "Sun" Registers have been on the market for over 5 years is the best evidence of the status of the patents and the character of the machine.

THE SUN MANUFACTURING CO.

Fig. 5-4: Sun 1896 catalog page telling about a certain cash register concern that claims to control every patent "that mortal man has ever thought of . . ."

Even the Hallwood guarantee was unique, to say the least:

> The Hallwood Register is guaranteed free from defects in either workmanship or material, and will be kept in perfect working order for three years free of cost, providing it is not abused by the Bullet and Horse Hair salesmen of the NCR Co.![10]

This refers to the tactics described in Figure 5-2.

NCR did, apparently, engage in buying up large quantities of competitive machines as shown in Figure 5-3.

That was the year 1905. If NCR could have gathered 2700 Hallwoods as shown in the ad circular, it must have been a phenomenal campaign for market share. NCR took great pains to show affidavits of ex-Hallwood employees that National's used Hallwoods were as good as new, and they were offered at 60% off retail. It was obviously intended to dry up Hallwood retail sales. If the average repurchase price were $50, NCR had $135,000 in capital tied up in this program—and that was just for Hallwood machines.

In March, 1897, NCR sued the Hallwood Company for infringement of its Maxwell patent which protected a device that locked all the keys on a register while the drawer was open (key arrester). A similar suit was entered against the New Columbus Watch Company as manufacturers of parts for the infringing machines. The Hallwood Company countersued, alleging unfair competition and conspiracy to restrain trade.

Here is yet another technique, as disclosed in court testimony by Hugh Chalmers:

> Q. Mr. Chalmers, do you know of any particular patents, or can you give now any particular patents for improvements that were taken out on competitors' machines? . . . against the Hallwood . . .
>
> A. Yes. . . . We took out a patent upon a check printing device [connected] to a Hallwood machine. . . . We told him [a National patent attorney] to put a check printing device . . . upon the Hallwood machine . . . in about 1902 or 03.[11]

In other words, National used the practice of blocking Hallwood from adding features to *its own registers* by patenting National add-ons to Hallwood machines before Hallwood could get to it!

The flurry of law suits lasted 18 years, during which time the Hallwood Company went out of business. Henry Hallwood retained ownership of the patents under which his company had operated. With them he formed the International Manufacturing Co. This in turn was succeeded by a number of other companies, the last of which was the American Cash Register Company, which NCR then sued again.

The Sun Manufacturing Company

Sun evolved from the Waddel Wooden Ware Works which made a register based on a very different principle than the press-down key approach of Ritty and National. Its predecessor, the Simplex, was active well before NCR was a powerhouse. National tried at least once in court to overcome the Sun patents around 1894-5, but failed. Eventually, NCR acquired Sun.

U. S. v. NCR Antitrust Suit

In 1910 representatives of the American Company struck back in a different way. They appeared before the Department of Justice in Washington in 1910 and filed a complaint against NCR.

A civil suit was filed against NCR by United States Attorney General Wickersham in December, 1911, in the U.S. District Court in Cincinnati, based largely on the theory of restraint of trade. In February, 1912, the United States Grand Jury issued an indictment against Patterson and many other NCR officials, charging them with criminal conspiracy under the Sherman Antitrust Law.[12]

The Government contended that NCR was doing 95% of all cash register business and charged that this was a monopoly. After a trial on February 13, 1913, the jury returned a verdict of guilty on all counts. Small fines and short jail sentences were imposed on each of the defendants. Patterson himself was fined $5000 and sentenced to one year in jail. Immediate plans were made to appeal, and then an amazing quirk of nature and fate occurred.

A great flood broke upon Dayton, wreaking devastation and disorder on the town. The waters of the Miami, Stillwater and Mad rivers overflowed at the same time. Patterson kicked all of his resources into action in order to organize assistance for the victims. The NCR plant was converted into an instant haven of refuge, and overnight, Patterson became a national figure. Hundreds of people sent messages to President Wilson urging him to pardon Patterson in recognition of his great humanitarian work during the flood.

As soon as he heard of this activity, Patterson sent the following telegram to the President:

> Our case is still in the courts. I do not ask for, nor would I accept, a pardon. All I want is simple justice.[13]

The United States Court of Appeals heard the case beginning in October, 1914 and the decision was handed down on March 13, 1915. In effect, the Appeals Court overruled the use of the long history of abuses presented by the Government and it held that the sole issue was whether NCR had conspired, in the manner charged, against the American Cash Register Company *within the three years immediately preceding the indictment*. The case was remanded to the trial court.

In Marcossen's own words,

> It so happened that I sat alongside John H. Patterson on that fateful March morning in 1915. He had asked me to be with him on a day that would spell triumph or disaster for him. He sat unperturbed during the reading of the 57-page decision. When Judge Cochran uttered the words,
> "We are constrained, therefore, to reverse the judgement of the lower court . . . "
> He did not show a trace of emotion.[14]

While this was an important reversal for Patterson, it did not clear away the civil suits that were pending. Instead of pressing the

arduous process of trials and appeals, the Government and NCR defendants agreed that the Government would not pursue the criminal matters and NCR entered into a consent decree with the Government to settle the civil case. That consent decree still stands in 1987.

Competition and the 1912 Antitrust Lawsuit

Much has been said about the turn-of-the-century competitive practices of the companies that grew dominant in their industries. NCR was an prototypical example. There is irony in the fact that a U.S. federal antitrust lawsuit tried in 1911-12 did wonders in preserving valuable historical information about NCR, the cash register industry and other specific business equipment companies.

Without the 2,100 pages that document that lawsuit, this book would have been much more difficult to assemble than it was already. NCR, itself, has been intransigent over the years in not allowing the use of its copious files on NCR and competitive machines for reasons not fully understood by the authors, even after several attempts.

Much of the information extracted from the sworn testimony of the 1912 antitrust lawsuit has been used elsewhere in this book. In this section, the essence of the lawsuit will be illustrated using several quotes extracted verbatim.

Those who have studied the cash register, or who have collected them, have been aware of the stories about the competitive practices used by NCR. Many of the tales the author has heard are retold here unaltered by years of hand-me-down story-telling, captured by federal attorneys back in 1911 when the action was still fresh in the minds of the injured parties.

To start, the indictment filed February 22, 1912, in the District Court of the United States of America for the Southern District of Ohio had several counts that extend over many pages. Excerpts give a flavor of the competitive environment at the time:

> INDICTMENT—Filed February 22, 1912
> In the District Court of the United States of

America for the Southern District of Ohio, Western Division.

. . . throughout the twenty years last past, inventors and manufacturers have been busy inventing, producing and putting upon the market divers record-keeping and cash-receptacle devices, usually called cash registers, each consisting generally of a box, principally of metal, but partly of wood, glass and other materials, containing a drawer or recess for the holding of coins and paper money, and a mechanism, manipulated by outside keys or similar means, for the use of employes in registering, for the information of the proprietor, upon a concealed and locked record, the sales made by employes of the business concern making use of the device, and at the same time visibly indicating the amount of each sale or the character of each transaction; the recording or registering devices being so connected with the lock of the money-drawer that when any of said devices is operated the money-drawer is unlocked and opened, so that money can be placed therein and change extracted therefrom; said money-drawer being automatically locked upon being closed, and the interior mechanism of said registering device being protected by a lock, the key of which is retained by the proprietor, from being interfered with by unauthorized persons . . .

That of the total amount of manufacturing of such cash registers done by all of said concerns during said twenty [1892-1912] years, said The National Cash Register Company has done from approximately eighty per cent early in said period to approximately ninety-five per cent at the latter end thereof. . . .

. . . [the defendants] knowingly engaged and consciously participated in a corrupt conspiracy in undue, unreasonable, direct and oppressive restraint of said interstate trade and commerce. . . . have unlawfully, wrongfully and irresistibly excluded others from engaging in that trade and commerce, none of which has been justified or warranted by any letters-patent, a description of which conspiracy and means is now here set forth:

1. The inducing, hiring and bribing of employes and ex-employes of said competitors of said The National Cash Register Company deceitfully and wrongfully to disclose to said The National Cash Register Company the secrets of the business of the concerns by which they were respectively employed . . .

2. The inducing, hiring and bribing of employes of carters, truckmen, express companies, railroad common carriers, telegraph companies and telephone companies, wrongfully and unlawfully to disclose to said The National Cash Register Company the secrets of the business of such carters, truckmen, express companies, railroad common carriers, telegraph companies and telephone companies, pertaining to the carriage and transportation of cash registers for such competitors, . . .

4. The using of the influence of said The National Cash Register Company and of its agents with, and the making of unwarranted and false statements to, banking and other institutions, to injure the credit of said competitors and prevent their securing and accommodations of money, credit and supplies convenient and necessary to the carrying on of their business.

5. The instructing and requiring of all sales agents of said The National Cash Register Company to interfere with, obstruct and prevent, in every way possible, sales of such competitive cash registers by said competitors, and by agents of said competitors . . .

. . . and particularly by making to prospective purchasers of such competitive cash registers false and unwarranted statements derogatory of the same, and false, libelous and unwarranted statements reflecting injuriously upon the business character and financial credit of such competitors . . .

. . . and offering to sell and selling, to such prospective purchasers of cash registers from said competitors, genuine cash registers of said The National Cash Register Company at prices much less than the regular and standard prices therefor and upon unusually favorable terms as to payments and deferred payments; by inducing, through such false, libelous and unwarranted statements and through said unusual offers, persons who had already ordered such competitive cash registers to cancel such orders and purchase the genuine cash registers of said The National Cash Register Company . . .

. . . by inducing, through such false, libelous and unwarranted statements, in some cases persons who had bought and paid for such competitive cash registers, and in other cases persons who had only partially paid for such cash registers, to surrender the same to said The National Cash Register Company in exchange for genuine cash registers of that company upon such a basis that those persons would lose nothing on account of their having so purchased such competitive cash registers, for the purpose of exhibiting, and thereupon actually exhibiting, such competitive cash registers, so obtained in exchange, in the windows of stores wherein genuine cash registers of said The National Cash Register Company were on sales, using placards, in some cases with the word "Junk" printed thereon, in other cases with the words "For Sale at Thirty Cents on the Dollar" printed thereon, and in still other cases bearing words of similar import derogatory of and damaging to said competitive cash registers; by exhibiting and offering for sale to some prospective purchasers of cash registers, cash registers in similitude of any particular competitive cash register any such prospective purchaser was contemplating buying, and this at a price in all cases much lower than the regular price of such competitive cash register and in some cases at a price much less than the manufacturer's cost of such competitive cash register, which cash register so exhibited and offered for sale to such prospective purchaser as aforesaid was one manufactured by said The National Cash Register Company, solely as a so-called "knocker," in such close similitude of the competitive cash register in question as to enable the sales agents of said The National Cash Register Company to represent to such prospective purchaser, and impel prospective purchaser to believe, as was often done, that it was in fact a cash register of such cheap and poor construction that it would be a waste of money to purchase it or the competitive cash register to which it was similar, such manufacture of such "knocker" by said The National Cash Register Company being discontinued when it was no longer useful as "knocker;"

. . . and, finally, by instructing and requiring sales agents of said The National Cash Register Company, and persons employed for that purpose by that company, secretly to weaken and injure the interior mechanism, and remove and destroy parts of such mechanism, of such competitors' cash registers in actual use by purchasers as they could by any means get their hands upon . . .

6. The making, in some cases, by said The National Cash Register Company, to such competitors, and to purchasers and prospective purchasers of such competitive cash registers, of threats to begin suits in the courts against them for infringing and for having infringed its patent rights pertaining to its genuine cash registers, when as said defendants each well knew, no such patent rights existed and no such suit was contemplated or would really be begun, and such threats were made merely to harass such competitors, purchasers and prospective purchasers . . .

7. The beginning, in other cases, by said The National Cash Register Company, against such competitors, and against purchasers of such competitive cash registers, of suits for infringement of patent rights of said The National Cash Register Company pertaining to its genuine cash registers, when in those cases . . . no patents upon which suits could be maintained were in existence . . . but all such suits would be kept pending only as long as they served the purpose of harassing such competitors and purchasers:

8. The organizing of cash-register manufacturing concerns and cash-register sales concerns, and the maintaining of them, ostensibly as competitors of said The National Cash Register Company, but in fact as convenient instruments for use in gaining the confidence and obtaining the secrets of said real competitors of said The National Cash Register Company and accomplishing the objects of said unlawful conspiracy; and the making of such use, also, of competitive concerns the ownership and control of which said The National Cash Register Company from time to time secured by the means aforesaid, and this as long as the fact of such ownership and control by said The National Cash Register Company could be kept secret:

9. The inducing, by offers of much greater compensation than they were receiving from said competitors respectively, agents and servants of said competitors, and dealers patronizing said competitors exclusively to leave the employment of said competitors or cease patronizing said competitors, to enter the employment of or patronize exclusively,

said The National Cash Register Company; and this principally for the purpose of embarrassing said competitors and restraining their said interstate trade and commerce:

10. By applying, and causing applications to be made, for letters-patent of the United States, in some cases upon the cash registers of said competitors and in other cases upon improvements upon such competitive cash registers, and this merely for the purpose of harassing such competitors by interference proceedings and suits and threats to institute such proceedings and suits. . . .

VERDICT—Filed February 13, 1913.
We, the jury, herein do find the defendants, John H. Patterson, Edward A. Deeds, George C. Edgeter, Willian F. Bippus, William H. Muzzy, William Pflum, Alfred A. Thomas, Robert Patterson, Thomas J. Watson, Joseph E. Rogers, Alexander C. Harned, Frederick S. High, Pliny Eves, Arthur A. Wentz, George E. Morgan, Charles T. Walmsley, Charles A. Snyder, Walter Cool, Myer N. Jacobs, Mont L. Lasley, Earl B. Wilson, Jonathan B. Hayward, Alexander W. Sinclair, John J. Range and M. G. Keith, W. M. Cummings, J. C. Laird, W. C. Howe and E. H. Epperson, guilty in manner and form as charged in each of the three counts of said indictment.

(Signed) R. E. Morrow, Foreman.[15]

To elaborate more fully on the technique stated of "weakening" a competitor's machine, one story goes like this: Competitive machines taken in by NCR would go through a refurbishment. The register would be shined up to look good, but critical brass or steel gears would be replaced with fiber gears. The registers were then sold via Watson's second hand stores (a disguised National front) at much lower prices than the nearby competitive store front (whether they were selling new machines or even second-hand machines).

The effect was a double blow. The low-priced sales knocked out the adjacent competitive register shops and then the doctored registers would fail within months, thereby causing a bad reputation for the manufacturer. Of course, a National representative would immediately appear on the scene to give a generous trade-in

on a new NCR. The customer, while spending much more money than desired, was relieved that National bailed him out of a bad purchase.

As mentioned elsewhere, the court decision was eventually overturned on appeal for several specific reasons including the fact that the anti-competitive actions took place prior to three years before the filing of the lawsuit.

NCR Views on Monopolies

One exhibit of the lawsuit printed in *N.C.R.*, the National house organ, dated March 15, 1892, had a fascinating view of monopolies:

Monopolies.
In the event of some one coming at you with the statement, "Why, my dear sir, I am opposed to monopolies, and The National Cash Register Company is seeking to foster one, thus keeping up the price of their machines, beyond a fair margin of profit and compelling the purchaser to pay this added cost, by reason of their monopoly," an argument in contra might be used something like this: First, give the "Wheat Field or Forest" arguments, showing how we have pioneered the business, and are now seeking only to maintain our rights and possessions. Then go further, by saying, that aside from our legal and vested rights to the exclusive control of the cash register business[!], monopolies are not such grievous things after all, for in the maintenance of a monopoly by the Standard Oil Company, the reduction of coal oil from 20 cents to 6 cents per gallon has been made possible thus benefiting the consumer to that extent. Nothing but the large aggregation of capital, by the Standard Oil Company, has brought this about. It has enabled them to build pipe lines to the larger cities and the sea-board, for transporting the oil, at a minimum carriage charge. Otherwise, the railroad companies would carry it under existing freight rates, which are, necessarily, much higher than piping it and the consumer would be compelled to stand the additional cost. Furthermore, their capital has permitted them to introduce other labor and money saving means, which, without it and the control of the market, could not have been accomplished. The consumer, therefore, would be compelled to pay out of his own pocket what is saved by means of centralization of power and money.

Cite, also, the Western Union Telegraph Company, how its vast capital has been used to buy out and consolidate other lines, which under one great head and management, has reduced tolls to a minimum. Had the old system prevailed, of many small lines—say in existence between here and San Francisco—each company would have demanded an arbitrary toll, thus increasing the cost of the message out of all proportion to what it is now. This was the case before the consolidation of all lines into the Western Union.

The fact that there are so many different lines of railroads in existence, causes freight rates to be higher than they would be, if there was a consolidation of all lines, for the same reason, given above.

Then go on to say that The National Cash Register Company is only making a fair margin of profit, to which it is entitled in the conduct of a legitimate business. It is permitted, by reason of having no competition of consequence, to put the best material and workmanship possible, in its registers, and give full value for the money asked. If there were numerous and strong competitors in the field, there would necessarily be a reduction in the price, and a reduction in the price means a cheapening of material and of labor, and a consequent deterioration of the register. The conditions of affairs, therefore, would be a good deal worse for the purchaser than at present. When buying anything of this kind, buy only the best; and from the fact that a purchaser is enabled to save anywhere from fifty cents to one dollar and a half per day, by use of a cash register, there are none so poor but what they can purchase and pay for a register.[16]

Of course, one of the dangers of monopolies is that innovation suffers because of a lack of competitive pressure. This is nowhere better stated than by John Patterson, himself, in the May 1, 1892 *N.C.R.* magazine:

I presume that there are about fourteen or fifteen different styles of registers in an embryo state, waiting to come upon the market. When they appear, we will jump onto them and knock them out.

Jno. H. Patterson.

We have four experimental departments working on patents, some of which we may not put on the market for two or three years to come. We don't believe in making improvements faster than

competition forces us to. We don't want to sell a cheap register because it won't protect a man's business.

Jno. H. Patterson.[17]

Knockers

The words "knocker" and "knockout" were used to refer to the practice of getting a competitive register out of a customer shop even on an uneconomic basis.

Knocker stories abound from the U. S. vs. NCR lawsuit:

N.C.R. May 1, 1892. Page 554.
The more opposition registers put on the market, the more we will knock out. Whenever I hear of a new machine, it don't scare me, because I know that we are able to duplicate it—to put a knocker on it—a better register at a less price—and in that way to discourage and kill it.

F. J. Patterson

Page 555.
Whenever you see an opposition advertisement in a newspaper, send it to us, because we can then put in an advertisement beside it, that will kill it.

R. S. Fowler

In knocking out an opposition register by the use of a "knocker," it is desirable to accomplish one of three results: The first and best thing to do, of course, is to knock it out before it gets into use. The next is to disgust the purchaser in order that he will send it back to the manufacturer and buy one of our regular registers, or to so disgust him with the opposition register, that he will send it back to the maker and not buy anything. As a last resort, knock out his opposition register, and sell him a knocker. This last is the least desirable victory to be achieved, but we would rather have you do that than not to knock out the opposition register at all.

J. H. Crane

The first man we want to make suffer in this knock-out fight is the agent selling the register. We propose to cut the price on knockers so low that the manufacturers can't afford to pay a living commission. As soon as the opposition agent ceases to make money, he is going to quit.

J. H. Crane.

N.C.R. March 15, 1892. Page 519.
Nos. 24 and 25 are knockers. Sell some to show
Peck and the American that we mean business. If
sold, we wish to get a testimonial. We are making
one hundred No. 24s and one hundred No. 25s,
and are able to furnish samples to the sales agents.
If needed in your territory, order a sample. These
registers are knockers for the American, made at
Chicago, Ill., and at Charlevoix, Mich., and they
may also be used as a knocker for the Peck register,
made at Syracuse, N.Y. The American sometimes
has a small railing on top. We will put this on our
knocker, if you so order. You may assure outsiders,
that we are prepared to make these registers in
large quantities.[18]

From the testimony of J. A. Sundwall, who
worked for NCR as a knockout man in 1892, and
subsequently, became an independent dealer:

In the knockout department, I was acting in the
capacity of a bogus drummer, with the cigar firm
of Wright & Glasgow, but I was not receiving
instructions from that firm. I was receiving instructions from The National Cash Register Company,
Dearborn street, Chicago. What I did was to apparently sell the cigars for the purpose of getting an
opening to the business at hand, where there was
a Lamson, the predominating opposition cash
register at that time being the Lamson; and if it
had been delivered to the particular prospective
customer that I was to call upon, I would—
(interrupted by objection). Those instructions were
given me by A. A. Adler, captain of the so-called
knockout department of the cash register company, Dearborn Street, Chicago. I was furnished in
the morning with the instructions from A. A. Adler,
from the office aforesaid, to call upon a list of
prospective customers of Lamson cash registers. I
did many things. I don't know what you want me
to say I was to do. I was supposed to do my duty
as knockout man, in the knockout work. I can only
repeat to be just and truthful in the matter, what I
said before, that I went to the prospective
purchaser, having been furnished a list by the
captain of the opposition department. I saw that
particular customer, forgetting the names now, I
have not got them on my tongue's end. That was
not my duty to remember. I had them in written

form, so that I could turn them in as a report to
the general office, what my success had been and
the nature of my visit with a particular party in
that particular place, and said reports I turned in
on that very same day. I kept on turning in such
reports daily. What I did was, I first tried to introduce myself as a cigar man, incidentally touching
on the subject of his so-called unlawful use of a
Lamson cash register. I would say, "Mr. Jones, I see
you have one of those unlawful cash registers in
use. Have you bought it? Aren't you afraid to use
that cash register? No, I guess not, the man just
put it in here yesterday." I would say, universally
speaking, that John Jones on Orchard Street, at
such and such a place, got into trouble about
using a Lamson cash register. "I suppose it is all
right, as good as any of them, perhaps better; but
you had better look into the fact before you pay
any money on it," etc. "You might lose it." I would
not say much, not enough to be identified as a
cash register man. I would try to stick to the idea
that I was a cigar salesman, which I was not, that
part of it was bogus, and perpetuated as such by
The National Cash Register Company.[19]

NCR built machines at times that were intended
to obliterate one specific competitive machine.
These were the real knockers, as described by
Joseph Warren, an assistant in the NCR Competition Department:

. . . if we had severe competition, we would have to
build a machine to meet that competition. We
called it a National machine. It was the same as
the new machine in shape and everything else, the
same key arrangement and operated the same
way. Such special machines were made meeting
the competition of the Hallwood, Union and many
others.[20]

The phrases "knockout men" and "knockers"
were early terms used in the early to mid-1890's,
but had been eliminated from the vocabulary by
1899 as if by positive intent. Then, competition
men were called "special men," trained and
managed from Dayton to use special knowledge
about competitive machines to defeat them.

Always it was emphasized that knocking out
was different than trading out. With the latter,
NCR would take in a competitive machine and
some cash for a National. With knocking out, it

Fig. 5-5: Here is an extant knocker register still owned by NCR. It is curiously used as a prop for a photo of NCR's current chairman, Charles E. Exley, Jr., and published in a May 5, 1986 *Business Week* article on NCR. While Exley told the photographer that this register was never put on the market, he may not have known the real reason why. This register was created by NCR in 1892 as a knocker to intimidate the Kruse Cash Register Co. into selling out (see Chapter 9).

was willing to take a loss on the transaction just to get the competitive machine out.

One NCR flyer claimed that from its own trade-in stocks

Cash registers of other makes are available at big discounts. Our entire stock of several thousand Hallwood registers taken in exchange as part payment for Nationals has now been reduced to 40c on the dollar. We also have in stock upwards of ten thousand registers of other makes such as Union, Sun, Ideal, Weiler, etc. All money paid for one of these registers bought of us will be allowed on the purchase of a new National anytime within 90 days of the sale of the machine.[21]

From Hugh Chalmers who was V.P. and General Manager of NCR in 1906, we hear:

We had a great many different kinds of machines, and when a competing machine was placed upon the market, we would discuss which one of these machines if we had one, would be best suited to meet that competition. If we did not have any machine to meet it, we would build one in the inventions department. The way we would meet competition in the field was that if a man was offering an Ideal register or a Hallwood register, or a register of any other make, we salesmen would have one that would have all the functions that that machine would have, that he would sell for less price than the other machine was offered. In the parlance of The National Cash Register Company such a machine was called by a number. . . . Our price was always based on the price of the competition machine and never upon the cost of manufacture. . . .

As to the Ideal, there was nothing done in reference to building a machine in competition, because we already had one and used the one we had.

In the case of the Hallwood with its improvements, there was something done in reference to putting on the market a register in competition with that . . .

There was nothing done with reference to putting a register on the market in competition with the Weiler. There was something done . . . with respect to the Union. What was done in respect of McGraw, Union or Hallwood, was that we built a model ourselves that would accomplish all the other machines accomplished and as nearly like it as we could . . . in appearance and in the function that the machine performed . . . I do not necessarily mean that we copied the mechanism of that machine; I don't think we copied; we worked around the patents of those companies largely. . . .

I remember that number 74 and 75 machines were used in competition with the Hallwood.

There were different machines at different times gotten out to meet the Hallwood competition; the numbers were 74 and 75. They were handle-operating machines. These machines did not substantially differ at all from [standard NCR models with similar features] . . . except they sold at one-half the price, practically the same machine at one-half the price. . . . They had slip printing devices on the side. . . . The resemblance between the No. 74 and 75 and the Hallwood machines was such that an expert could tell the difference; I don't think a layman could, except that the word "National" was on the drawer of the National and "Hallwood" on the drawer of the Hallwood.[22]

Chalmers also testified:

We [NCR] employed a number of Hallwood agents in 1900. . . . These men were all in the employ of the Hallwood Cash Register Company at the time we employed them.[23]

A special knocker catalog was produced in 1892 that pictured many competitive machines and the NCR weapon against them. That would be a great find to collectors since the NCR knocker machines were often numbered out of sequence and accordingly were one of the main reasons that made hash outof model numbering predictability.

In 1892, sixty-three competitive companies were in business and in 1895, double that many is estimated. Fifty to sixty brand names were produced in Detroit alone, although Detroit was an unusual hotbed of low-priced registers. As of June, 1895, NCR records showed 136 other companies had formed to enter the business since 1886.[24] Combined output of the 136 companies was estimated at $2,895,000. At that time, NCR estimated its output at 60 registers per day vs. 1 register per day for all its competition put together.[25]

Thomas Watson and NCR Second-Hand Stores

Thomas Watson Sr. joined NCR as a salesman in Buffalo, New York in October of 1895. He was to become a protege of Patterson, only to leave NCR in favor of an even more impressive task: the making of IBM.

In 1903 he was selected to head a new secret NCR subsidiary. The purpose was to gain control of the second-hand cash register industry. The Watson Cash Register and Second Hand Exchange had as its purposes to secretly buy out the second-hand stores for National, and to create havoc amongst targeted competitors.

An example of how this technique was used is provided by the Brainin Cash Register Co. of New York. No matter how hard they tried, NCR could not buy them. Sometime in 1904, Watson was able to accomplish under his own name what NCR couldn't. It was a matter of pride and emotion that caused Brainin not to want to sell to NCR. It's unimaginable what Brainin must have thought when he subsequently found out that he had actually sold to National.[26]

The technique Watson used was to rent a store front immediately next to the target second-hand store. Then, using NCR's vast stock of used non-NCR machines, he would undercut the adjacent store no matter how low they went until he drove them to selling their business or going bankrupt.

It is interesting to note the inventory of one second-hand register shop acquired directly by NCR in 1905, operated by an Isaac Freeman of San Francisco:

1	Chicago, new	3	Detroit
30	Weilers, new	23	Worlds
2	Lamsons #70685, 72026	8	United States
1	Century #2298	1	Standard
1	Metropolitan	3	Kruse
1	Peerless	13	Bensingers
3	Merchants	23	Imperials
1	Miller	8	Autographic & Standards
2	Security	2	Osborne
3	Seymour	2	Boston
4	Simplex	36	NCR registers[27]

In 1905, Watson changed the name of his operation to another front name, The American Second-Hand Cash Register Co. making it seem even more opposed to NCR. In 1906, NCR repurchased all the Watson stores, their job apparently having been completed.[28]

Other big second-hand shops bought by NCR were the Foss Novelty Co. of Cleveland and the Southern Cash Register Co. of Atlanta. Both of these were prime dealers in new Americans, as well as used machines of all makes.[29]

Watson became enormously popular with the NCR sales force and Patterson reportedly grew envious. Watson became confident and began to oppose some of Patterson's policies.

PLACARDS

Various Placards Carried in Stock

Placard No. 2 is wrapped two placards to a set. Placard No. 6 is wrapped two placards to a set. Placard No. 7 is wrapped two to a set. Placard No. 10 is not wrapped in sets.

Fig. 5-6: Here is the famous IBM motto "THINK," but this is a page from the NCR 1915 Trade-in Guide! The famous "THINK" was coined at NCR in the winter of 1911 by Thomas Watson, according to Frederick Fuller, *My Half Century as an Inventor*, p. 42. THINK signs went up everywhere at NCR, and eventually they were even sold to the public in placard form. He often said that the phrase "I didn't think" has cost the world millions of dollars. Thomas Watson must have carried the idea with him to IBM where it is prevalent.

In the fall of 1912 Watson voiced some of his disagreements in front of other NCR executives, and within weeks, he got the word he was no longer wanted. At age 40 he left NCR, reportedly saying:

> I've helped build all but one of those [NCR] buildings. Now, I am going to build a business bigger than John H. Patterson has.[30]

Watson found just what he wanted in the newly formed Computer-Tabulating-Recording Co., the result of the merging of Herman Hollerith's Tabulating Machine Co., the International Time Recording Co., the Dayton Scale Co. and Bundy Manufacturing Co.

Watson's first products were an adding tabulator, a sorter and a card punch. His training and philosophies acquired at NCR undoubtedly put him in good stead to make Computing-Tabulating-Recording Co. (renamed IBM in the 1920's) highly successful.

Street Fighting with Hallwood

Many other techniques were employed by National; some were highly ingenious and some were less eligible for compliment. A selection of intimidation techniques and "dirty tricks" stories against Hallwood that make fascinating reading can be found in the 1911 Federal Antitrust Suit against NCR.

Mr. Frank Walle, a grocery store owner in New Orleans purchased an American in late 1909 through the Larkin Specialty Co. by putting $20 down and agreeing to make payments up to the $105 purchase price. Then an NCR salesman called several times:

> The first man who called upon me after the purchase of the American said I had bought a piece of junk, and that they robbed me . . . Three or four days afterwards I went down to the salesroom. He introduced me to the local agent and took me into a side room and demonstrated to me by a machinist . . . The local representative said that this man was with the American for a number of years, and this American machine I bought was exactly like the one he was demonstrating. The

> one he was demonstrating was an *old* Hallwood. . . . He said that my American machine could never be repaired, because there was no one there to repair it, and that it would only be a question of time that the Larkin Specialty Company would not do any more business. He told me to cancel my contract and that they would pay the $20 difference, . . . I went to see Larkin and made complaint to him. . . . The National people never called on me after that. I kept the American machine and still have it.[31]

Mr. L. L. Des Bouillions, a merchant from Savannah, Georgia sold cash registers for the American Cash Register Co. from 1908 to 1909 on pure commissions:

> I had a consignment of about seven or eight registers. . . . I sold a machine to Peter Gisholm, and received a payment of $8, and in a week another payment of $12. He came to my office, and did not want the register any more. I afterwards went to his place of business. I found the register was not working. I saw a National register in the place of mine.
>
> During the period I have spoken of, I very frequently saw Mr. Stacey [of NCR] near me when I was going some place. When I would leave my office, I would go out and try to solicit for registers, and I would turn around and see someone walking maybe a block or two behind me. I saw Stacey at one time, and several other times I saw several other men, . . . There were so many of them, what they called opposition. . . .
>
> One time when I was in a customer's place of business, I saw Stacey's brother outside setting on a bicycle. He was a sub-agent for The National Cash Register Company. He was just leaning against a telegraph pole smoking. I was inside the store and he was directly outside on the sidewalk on a bicycle, leaning against a telegraph pole, waiting there, smoking, holding the machine up by his weight against the telegraph pole. His face was frequently turned toward me. . . .
>
> I stopped selling American cash registers when it was utterly impossible for me to do so, . . .[32]

Mr. Frederick Ladd had a cash register sales agency in Atlanta, Georgia, for Hallwood in 1905-06. It was called the Southern Cash Register Co.

The forged letter below is a fair sample of the many desperate methods unsuccessfully employed against the Hallwood Register.

REINER DRUGGIST.
E. LONG ST. NEAR 20TH COLUMBUS, O.

COLUMBUS, OHIO, ~~Sept 18,~~ 189~~7~~.

The National Cash Register Co.

Dayton, Ohio.

Gentlemen:

I have used three Hallwood Cash Registers, each succeeding one with the hope of getting a perfect machine, from my desire to patronize home industry; but I had to concede to superiority of the National, both in mechanical construction and operation, and have therefore purchased one of your No. 35 Registers, which gives perfect satisfaction.

Respectfully,

L. Reinert

I never wrote this letter and the signature to the same is a forgery

L. Reinert

Fig. 5-7: 1901 Hallwood catalog page reprint.

Mr. Sinclair [an NCR defendant in the anti-trust case] invited us up to the National office; said he had something he wanted to show us. We went up. As soon as we went in . . . he took us into a . . . demonstrating room and uncovered a register, which proved to be a Hallwood Leader. He demonstrated that register, made it out incorrect. . . . Mr. Sinclair demonstrated the register and spent about two hours or longer; made the register do much different from what the register we had on hand would do.

I told him he must have the register doctored. . . . So I went around behind the register and found the back was off. He then took his hand and took up the weights and showed us how the weights came up and down, how easily the register would wear out, and upon examination immediately I found that the springs were disconnected, and I told him he couldn't do that in the regular line of business, but that the register should be used as it was intended to be used. . . .

"You are two nice men, too well known in Atlanta to handle a register of that character" [NCR's Sinclair said]. I told him, "I will tell you, Mr. Sinclair, I think the register is all right; I just don't believe the register will do what you have made it do, unless an expert like yourself should take your hand and disconnect the springs of the cams."[33]

John Broomhall sold Hallwoods from 1902 to 1905 in Los Angeles. He remembered that in 1904 the National agent by the name of Floyd Hoyt said to Broomhall that the territory was not big enough for the two of them, and that he should come over to NCR:

. . . he [Hoyt] was compelled to follow me over the territory, as soon as he located me, keep directly on my trail, . . .

I remember an occurrence in Kruel's pharmacy in Los Angeles in 1905, when I was trying to sell a machine. . . . I had an appointment by telephone to visit Mr. Kruel. . . . I introduced myself to him, and that was about as far as I got, until I noticed the door darken and four men came in. . . . They were National agents. They simply brushed me aside . . . and told him "I am a National representative. I understand you are in the market for a cash register. . . ."

He told Mr. Kruel that I had no cash register, and said, "He has a bird cage here of wire and springs." I objected to that expression and he continued that I had no cash register and told me I was a liar if I said I had.

The next day . . . I had a machine in my buggy, and I drove to visit a Mr. Shapiro, set my machine on his counter, and a young man . . . approached me. He told the proprietor that there was no haste in buying a register immediately, that he should investigate. He told me he had telephoned Smith. Smith was the man I had the trouble with the day before at Kruel's pharmacy. I hurried the sale . . . got out into my rig as Smith and two other men I didn't know came out of their automobile, and into the store where I had been . . .[34]

National's tactics were picked up in a press story under outright humorous circumstances.

The following article appeared in its entirety in the *Los Angeles Commercial Bulletin*:

EXHIBIT 124.

Taken from the Commercial Bulletin of August 14, 1908.

SPOTTERS HOUND REGISTER MAN.

Dirty War Being Waged Against American Hallwood Cash Register Company in Los Angeles. Spotters Spy on Office and Follow Salesmen About.

For weeks the claim has been made to The Bulletin that the employes of The National Cash Register Co. have been resorting to disreputable tactics in an effort to embarrass and defeat the efforts of The American Hallwood Cash Register Co. to do business in southern California. The claim has repeatedly been made that employes of the National Company are maintaining a picket in front of the Hallwood Company's office at 643 South Spring st., that Hallwood employes are followed by employes of the National when they leave the office to solicit business or make deliveries and that as soon as the prospective customer is thus located every effort is made to prevent the Hallwood Company from making a sale. The Bulletin has been unwilling to believe that a company of the standing of The National Cash Register Co. would tolerate such despicable and un-American tactics. This week The Bulletin on its own account investigated the claims of the American Hallwood Company and this is what transpired:

By arrangement with Manager Waller of the Hallwood Company one of his employes Tuesday drove leisurely from the company's office at 643 South Spring street past The Bulletin office at 837 South Spring street. He was followed about a half block behind a man in a heavy runabout. The Bulletin man had a conveyance ready and followed the alleged spotter, the line-up being Hallwood man in the lead, spotter a half block behind and Bulletin man a close third. The Hallwood man quickly turned into Main street and doubled back from Ninth street to Seventh street on Main. At Seventh he turned abruptly around and again went out Main street to Ninth. The spotter followed every turn thus describing a double loop and proving conclusively that it was no chance driving but that he actually was following the Hallwood man in the runabout. At Ninth street the Bulletin man hailed the spotter. "Are you an employe of The National Cash Register Co.?" was asked without ceremony. Caught unawares he blurted out: "You bet I am." "Why are you following the man ahead?" he asked. By this time he realized his blunder and whipping up his horse answered, "Oh, they're crazy."

The one-two-three chase was renewed out East Ninth street, the Hallwood man trying to lose the National man and the National man very busy trying to lose The Bulletin man, yet at the same time following the leader. At Gladys Avenue a turn north was made and quickly followed by the spotter, but the Hallwood horse was the faster and by a quick turn into an alley the National man and The Bulletin man lost the scent. Then for about thirty minutes the self-confessed National employe drove this way and that covering thoroughly the business section between Los Angeles and Alameda, looking up and down at every turn for the large runabout driven by the Hallwood man. Finally the chase was given up.

Wednesday a further investigation was made, several merchants being interviewed. Here are the interviews:

Albert Walters, wall paper dealer, 627 South Spring street, a few doors north of the Hallwood office: ". . . I have seen enough of this spotter work to know that what Mr. Waller says is true.

"For weeks one or two men in various conveyances whose faces have long since become familiar to me have patrolled up and down this block or stood at the curb, often directly in front of my store, and always with their eyes on the Hallwood office. When a Hallwood runabout leaves the Hallwood office they follow in quick pursuit. It is dirty work."

H. Beadle, proprietor of the barber shop at 622 South Spring street:

"These men have used my barber shop and cigar stand in front as a hang-out for weeks. They are here to spot against the cash register company across the street and keep their eyes constantly on that office. They make no bones about their business and what they are here for. While they are good customers of mine and good fellows personally, I can't help saying it is dirty work."

Ernest Gerleman, grocer, 514 South Main street:

"Waller has been in to see me several times. Also several times he has pointed out to me men whom he said were following him. In front of my store he has started first up the street and then down and these men would follow him. This has occurred several times." The purpose of this espionage, according to Mr. Waller, is nothing short of driving his company out of business at any cost. Mr. Waller says in interview: "They watch our office and follow our wagons, and interfere in every way possible with our business. They try to prevent our making sales and if a sale is made attempt to make the purchaser think that he has been defrauded by offering to sell him a similar register at much less price.

"The purpose of this is to make the purchaser dissatisfied and to prevent him from recommending our machines and our company to his neighbors and friends. They have on many occasions made the statement that the Hallwood is out of business and that owners of our machines would not be able to get parts or repairs for same. They have followed me personally when I went to the bank or to lunch and when I went to call on customers. The other day one of my wagons drove up and down Spring street five times without a stop and it was followed at every turn. I am selling goods on the square and do business in a straightforward manner. I welcome competition but believe I am entitled to a square deal."

The Other Side.

Thursday of this week the National cash register employe who was No. 2 in the chase up and down Main street and out East Ninth called at The Bulletin office and introduced himself. His name is Chadwick. He explained that he supposed that an article was to appear in The Bulletin about the chase and that there were two sides to every question. The editor of The Bulletin had a press proof drawn of the above story and told him to read it over and if there were any misstatements in it which could be disproved they would immediately be corrected. Mr. Chadwick said he wanted the editor to meet Mr. Wilson, the local manager of the National company, who would explain the other side. The editor met Mr. Wilson, and a proof of the above story also was handed him with the same statement that if it was untrue in any particular and its truth could be disproved it would not be printed.

Mr. Wilson said: "There has been too much of this following of men done—more than I thought—but my men are eager for business and they may resort to things that I would not permit. However, we do believe that we have the right to know what our competitors are doing and that is what we have done. Every man watches his competitor— that's business. We have divided the city into districts and each salesman must look after his district and see to it that our competitors do not get the business. Since competition has come in, to relieve our regular men, we have put two men at seeing what the other people are doing.

But these men have never been authorized to picket the Waller office—I don't like the word picket. They simply have been authorized to watch competition and it seems that they have been going too far. However, the methods of the Hallwood company have for many years been such that almost any kind of competition seems justified against them. The company was organized years ago for the sole purpose of forcing the National to buy it and it has been a bitter fight. Some things have been done which ought not to have been done. It's a bitter fight."

Wilson then showed The Bulletin a large number of reproductions of defamatory circulars against the National Company and its methods printed several years ago by the Hallwood Company. Note the name Hallwood Company.

However, the Hallwood Company, which signed the circulars, has been out of business for several years and the company now in business here is The American Hallwood Company, said to be an entirely new corporation, which has purchased the patent rights of the old Hallwood. Therefore, these old accusations cannot be very successfully held against the new company.

Waller, the manager of the local new Hallwood agency, was also manager of the old agency, but his employers now are different. His conduct in this fight as far as the Bulletin has been able to ascertain, has been honorable in every particular. Also his record while with the old company is equally good.[35]

The Little Man and the Dragon

A final example of almost perverse humor from the *N.C.R.* magazine of July 15, 1892 (page 625) sums up this section:

> The Fable of the Little Man and the Dragon. Once upon a time there was a little Man who went out into the Woods to hunt. It so happened that these Woods belonged to a celebrated Dragon known as the N.C.R. The little Man knew this, but thought he'd Take his Chances.
>
> While sitting Down one Day enjoying himself with a little Consolation from the "Pump," the owner of the Property put in an Appearance. "Go, 'way, Mr. Dragon," said the Little Man, "These are My Woods." "Your Woods," answered the Dragon, "Not much! I have owned them for years." "Oh, no," said The Little Man, "I own them because I am on Them." "You do, eh," replied the Dragon, "well, I'll just yank You off Them," and so saying, he proceeded to Gobble the little man up.
>
> Moral—Go ask the Hopkins & Robinson and the Bensinger Companies for it![36]

Perspectives on John H. Patterson

John Patterson merits some specific attention in any survey of early cash registers. His innovative ideas and methods succeeded in establishing the National Cash Register Company as the dominant force in the industry. This industry grew with the company, as the cash register became an essential part of any well-run storefront business.

Patterson was idolized within his company and he became a legend. He was feared, respected, understood and misunderstood—typical of a leader with vision and unstoppable drive to establish his will above others.

Those who found themselves on his good side were accepted, cared for, amply compensated and made comfortable. Those who crossed him were eliminated—employees were fired, competitors were run out of business. Patterson came to believe that the cash register enabled a way of business life that was "right" as opposed to all other ways of conducting a business which were "wrong." With him, these were almost religious concepts—and this way of thinking included personal behavior as well.

Patterson is generally credited with inventing the steps associated with today's approach towards the "sales cycle" used by most professional sales forces. It was likely that John Patterson was the first to think of selling in process terms. Today, the famous sales forces of the high technology industries (IBM, Xerox, NCR and others) all use derivatives of his methods.

Part of Patterson's methods were the continual barrage of direct mail and advertising. So much mail from NCR would show up on prospect's desks that one response in May of 1886 was prompted as shown in Figure 6-2. Notice the terse, handwritten remark: "Let up, we never done you any harm."

John Patterson developed a template of the kind of person he wanted around and he engaged in all sorts of activity either to train people to his mold or to get rid of them. While it may be possible to find stories about how much of a humanitarian he was, the catch is that in many cases he was a humanitarian when it benefited him to benefit others. For instance, he is highly praised for how much he did to improve the town of Dayton, Ohio, but his motive seemed to be to make a better place for the headquarters of his company. He was fanatical about satisfying clients—but that was to insure the sale of more cash registers. He was said to be a "pioneer in industrial welfare" (the title of a book written by NCR historian Samuel Crowther in 1926), but that was only true in the eyes of the employees who retained their jobs.

In another history written by Isaac Marcossen many examples are given of how ruthless Patterson could be about terminating people's jobs.

> On one occasion he called in a foreman to get a report on the work in his department. The man said: "I am glad to report that we are 100% efficient, the men are loyal and the best we can get. Our product is as perfect as can be made."
>
> "Then you are perfectly satisfied," said Patterson.
>
> "Yes sir, I am."
>
> "All right," retorted Patterson, "you are fired."[1]

In the John H. Patterson code, no one should be completely satisfied.

Patterson was opposed to free enterprise and fair competition—the very environment that permitted his own beginnings and fostered his growth. He believed that he had a right to all of the cash register business. He believed his ownership of patents gave him a monopoly and

Fig. 6-1a: John Patterson portrait reproduced from
Crowther's *John Patterson, Pioneer in Industrial Welfare.*

he was incensed at the idea that there were competitors. He didn't relish the idea of competition and he used every means to eliminate it. He had his own sense of ethics that was of the school that it doesn't matter how you get there—it's the end result that counts.

Patterson's style of getting things done is surely part of the corporate behavior pattern in the early 1900's that gave rise to unions for the protection of employees and antitrust laws for the protection of free and fair competition.

Marcossen described Patterson as

Almost undersized, he was wiry, with grey eyes, florid complexion, sandy hair and bristling moustache. He was, as someone put it, "a little

Badge worn by the members of
Class No. 50, Agents' Training School,
during their session at the factory.

Fig. 6-1b: Competitive tenacity, a hallmark of NCR sales training. This decorated indicator tag from an article in the *NCR*, National's house magazine, says it all!

man with a dynamo inside." Dominated by a ruthless will, and driven by a restless energy, he was both a doer and a dreamer. . . . Divorced from his eccentricities he stood revealed as a great leader and teacher of men. He made men as well as machines.[2]

S. C. Allyn joined NCR in 1913 and became president in 1941. He continued as president and then chairman of the board for 20 years before retirement. In an undated monograph produced by a Dayton bank, Allyn recalls,

. . . a $50,000 shipment of registers had been returned from England, labelled DEFECTIVE. The materials were good, and the engineering correct. What, then, was the trouble?

Always capable of spectacular action, Mr. Patterson moved his desk into the factory. The complaints he heard from the workers, the shameful conditions he saw with his own eyes started him on the program of "welfare work" . . . he cleaned up the plant, designed the first "daylight" factory buildings in America, organized worker-education classes, . . .

It worked, and no more faulty machines left NCR. . . .

"It pays," was Mr. Patterson's blunt excuse for what he was doing. He was not a man of abstract idealism or a pretender to great humanitarianism. He

simply saw what so many leaders of his era failed to see. More money could be made by treating employees fairly . . .

. . . he was colorful—not out of egotistical desire to attract attention to his person, but because he knew that men would remember a lesson only if it were delivered in grandly graphic terms.[3]

On second thought, there might have been a few occasions on which he played to the gallery in the style of a fearsome tycoon. A waiter at the Waldorf once snatched away a course sooner than he expected, and he threw the staff into a panic by demanding a hammer and nails and threatening to nail the next set of plates to the table. . . .[4]

My first promotion came as a result of Mr. Patterson's tempestuous personality.

It was customary for executives to lunch periodically at Far Hills, the Patterson estate. One fateful day in 1916, a new assistant comptroller had joined the party and was asked by Mr. Patterson to say a few words.

The man hesitated. Mr. Patterson might have remembered the time a salesman began a presentation with the words, "I'm no good at public speaking"—and he, Mr. Patterson, had snapped, "If you're no good at it, then sit down." At any rate, the comptroller attempted to excuse his ineptness by mumbling that his "soup was getting cold." Mr. Patterson was very stony, and said, "By all means, eat your soup!" Everyone in the room knew that the job of assistant comptroller had, at that moment, become available again.

Next day, the job was offered to me.

It has been said that every major American firm has had at least one executive who was trained, and probably fired, by John H. Patterson.[5]

Allyn recalls further,

I won't forget the day Mr. Patterson announced that Five was a somehow mystical number. There were five senses, he pointed out, also five fingers to a hand, five points to a star, five aspects to every man: the financial, the social, the mental, the moral, the physical. He was obsessed by Five, and for days on end we prepared variations on the theme.[6]

Patterson's competitive methods can be seen close-up in excerpts from testimony by three other prominent personalities in the cash register business: Hugh Chalmers, ex-general

Fig. 6-2: A collection of early mailers (#1-12) sent in rapid succession to 5,000 prospects.

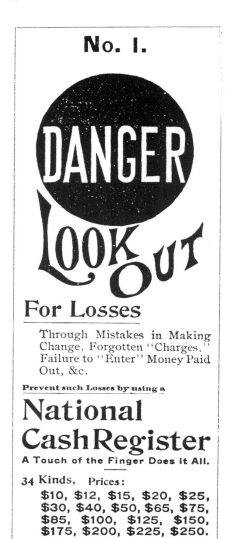

Figs. 6-3a, b, c: A series of ads used extensively in magazines and newspapers in 1892. Courtesy Smithsonian Institution.

manager of NCR, William McGraw, an ardent competitor, and Gustave Wineman, who was both a competitor and an employee at one time or another.

Hugh Chalmers

Hugh Chalmers was the vice president and general manager of National in the years 1903 to 1907. In that capacity, he worked directly for Patterson and obviously knew him well. Chalmers began his career in cash registers with National in 1888 until he left in July of 1907 to form the Chalmers Motor Co. His leadership skills at NCR were again confirmed at Chalmers Motor Co. since he managed to hold on to a personal ownership of 60% of his company

while expanding it to a $16-million-a-year enterprise, employing 4200 men after 5 years of operation. Chalmers also set up a competitive cash register subsidiary called the Michigan.

In Hugh Chalmers' own words, he recollected from his NCR days,

I was first office boy [in 1888], then successively clerk, stenographer, bookkeeper, office manager, city salesman, sales agent, assistant manger of agencies, manager of agencies, second vice president and general manager, vice president and general manager [December, 1902-July, 1907] . . . . I reported to Mr. Patterson. . . .

In the discussion of competition at the meetings of the district agents, I remember John H. Patterson used a circle on the blackboard as an illustration. I have heard him make the illustration when he

No. 7.

Be On Guard

Against Mistakes in Making Change, Forgotten "Charges," Failure to "Enter" Money Paid Out, &c.

These are the things that undermine a store-keeper's business. Prevent them by using a

National Cash Register

A Touch of the Finger Does it All.

—Over— in daily use
46,000 in all parts of the world.

We make 34 kinds of Cash and Autographic Registers.

Send for Catalogue and get posted.

PRICES:

$10, $12, $15, $20, $25, $30, $40, $50, $65, $75, $85, $100, $125, $150, $175, $200, $225, $250.

——— THE ———

National Cash Register Co.
DAYTON, OHIO, U. S. A.
New York Office, 1179 Broadway.

No. 8.

THINK IT OVER

—— 46,000 ——

National Cash Registers

are in daily use in all parts of the world, and you, who need it as much as the other 46,000 storekeepers, are trying to get along without one. *Don't keep it up longer; it's a losing game.*

A Touch of the Finger Does it All.

Catalogue and book of 1,001 testimonials Free.

34 kinds of Cash and Autographic Registers.

PRICES:

$10, $12, $15, $20, $25, $30, $40, $50, $65, $75, $85, $100, $125, $150, $175, $200, $225, $250.

THE

National Cash Register Co.
DAYTON, OHIO, U. S. A.
New York Office, 1179 Broadway.

No. 9.

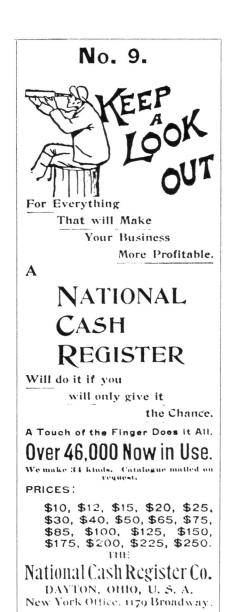

KEEP A LOOK OUT

For Everything
That will Make
Your Business
More Profitable.

A

NATIONAL CASH REGISTER

Will do it if you
will only give it
the Chance.

A Touch of the Finger Does it All.

Over 46,000 Now in Use.

We make 34 kinds. Catalogue mailed on request.

PRICES:

$10, $12, $15, $20, $25, $30, $40, $50, $65, $75, $85, $100, $125, $150, $175, $200, $225, $250.

THE

National Cash Register Co.
DAYTON, OHIO, U. S. A.
New York Office, 1179 Broadway.

---

talked with competitors, that our money came from all over the world from the sale of machines, and this money would naturally come in, in getting started, in certain sections, and we could put our machines on the market at lower profits, because our profits came from all over the world and that only one section was affected by competition.[7]

Chalmers is referring to a classic case of cross-subsidization. A court record of the kind of drawing Patterson would make is shown in Figure 6-4. This illustrates how profits from one area can be used to crush a competitor in another area with artificially low prices so that when the competitor is out of business, prices can be raised to desired levels.

Chalmers recalls further,

Mr. Patterson made a great many illustrations. I remember his dog story. It was: If you are going to

EXHIBIT 70.
N. C. R. October 1, 1897. Page 429.

Losses on opposite side of the globe
made up by gains here, while all the
rest of the company's offices are
making a profit.

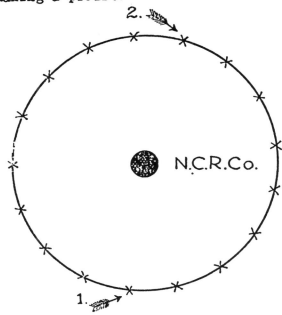

Temporary loss here on account of competition.

This circle represents the earth. The small crosses
represent the selling offices of The National Cash Register Company in every civilized country. Suppose compe-

Exhibit 71.
tition springs up in the territory pointed out by arrow No.
1. The National Cash Register Company can afford to
do business here at a loss if necessary to meet the competition, because the profit made at the office marked with
arrow No. 2 will make up for the loss, while all the other
offices of the company all over the civilized world will
make a profit and keep up the income of the Company to
its normal amount.

Fig. 6-4.

kill a dog, it would be much kinder to hit him on
the head instead of beginning with his tail and
cutting off an inch or two at a time. I have heard
that at different times, at conventions and before
competitors when competitors would visit the
factory . . .[8]

William T. McGraw

William McGraw was a driving force among the
Detroit competitors. He entered the cash register business in 1892-93 with the Seymour, and
then proceeded to form and manage the Detroit

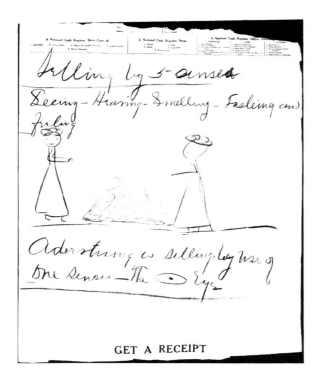

GET A RECEIPT

Fig. 6-5: Patterson's use of his rule of Five as applied to
explaining the use of advertising in selling. In his own
handwritten note, he says:
  "Selling by 5 Senses
  "Seeing-Hearing-Smelling-Tasting and Feeling
  "Advertising is selling by using one sense—the eye."

Cash Register Co., the Globe, and the Century.
His contact with Patterson was brief, but
intense. We have his verbatim recollection of
his meeting with Patterson in Dayton when
National was pressuring to buy out McGraw:

We went to luncheon at the Officers' Club. . . . John
H. Patterson came in. He took a seat at the table,
and the general conversation was that no company
could succeed against the organization of the
National Cash Register Company, and at that time,
Mr. Patterson told me that he was going to put out
a machine in competition with mine that would
sell for $35. I asked him this question, "Are you
going to brand that machine National Cash Register Company?" He said he intended to. I said, "Do
you mean you are putting that machine out to
sell?" He said, "yes." I said I would take all those
machines that he could manufacture and send
him a certified check for the amount, if they were
branded National Cash Register Company.

He said, "Do you think I would sell those

machines to you?" I said, "You are going to make
them to sell, aren't you?" He said, "Yes, but I won't
sell them to you." Just about that time he picked
up a large water bottle; sat it down; and said that
that represented the National Cash Register
Company. He then reached around and found a
little salt cellar, which was the smallest object on
the table, and set it down by the side of the water
bottle. He said, "Now, that represents the National
Cash Register Company; that salt cellar represents
you, and we will wipe you off the face of the earth,"
to use his exact language. . . .

Another thing Mr. Patterson said at that table
was, that there never was a cash register company
that made any money. I said, that I did not like to
dispute with him, but if he would send a competent man to Detroit, I would show him a company
[The Globe Cash Register Co.] that had declared
dividends more than their capital stock and had a
surplus that exceeded their capital stock. That was
before the conversation in regard to the water
bottle. . . .

Something was stated about our machine
infringing; that was standard; they always told us
our machine infringed. Mr. Patterson said our
machine was an infringement. I told him if they
would point out any portion of our machine that
was an infringement we would eliminate that
feature. I told them that not only that time, but a
great many other times. I want to correct that
statement. They did point out a feature that they
claimed was an infringement and we eliminated it.
That was some time afterwards. . . .

Afterwards we had several interviews [in the
summer of 1904] with Chalmers and Counsel-
man . . . we never could come to satisfactory terms.
I didn't want to sell out. . . .

They had a machine that was somewhat similar
to mine, in one of the rooms in the Cadillac Hotel
[in Detroit]. Chalmers said they had organized . . .
another concern, for the purpose of fighting the
concern we represented, and I think he said that
they had organized it in New Jersey and were
going to make that machine and sell it through
this concern, instead of the National Cash Register
Co., for the purpose of competing with my
machine, putting me out of business, to be plain
about it. I told Chalmers to go ahead; I wasn't
afraid of them.[9]

Of course, as described in volume II under the
Century Cash Register Co., Patterson did
succeed in buying out McGraw in 1905.

Gustave Wineman

Gustave Wineman seems to have been every-where in the cash register business. He was

Superintendent of the factory for Victory Cash Register Company (Detroit, Michigan)	1892–1896
Superintendent of the Osborn Cash Register Co. (Detroit, Michigan sold to NCR)	1896–1900
Manager and inventor for the Weiler Cash Register Co. (Detroit, Michigan sold to NCR)	1901–1906
Assistant Manager of the Union Cash Register Co. (Trenton, NJ., sold to NCR)	1906–1907
General Manager of NCR's Detroit Cash Register Works (Detroit, Michigan, this was the old Weiler plant)	1907
Founder and inventor for the Jewell Cash Register Co. (Detroit, Michigan, until it burned to the ground in 1911)	1908–1911

Wherever he went, NCR seems to have followed and bought out his employer. One could assume he was a competent factory manager. Eventually he formed his own company, the Jewell, but when it burned to the ground, he decided to call it quits.

Wineman is on record recalling a personal encounter with Patterson. At the time Wineman had just assumed general managership of the Detroit Cash Register Works for National:

Mr. Patterson addressed me, saying: "Mr. Wineman, where are you from?" I told him from Detroit. He asked me what I had done there. I told him I was manager of the Detroit Cash Register works for the National. He went on to ask me if I had any orders or contracts on hand of such a nature that it was absolutely necessary that they should be filled. I told him I didn't think so; however, I had just received an order from Mr. Blessing, which I had left instructions to fill as much as possible, and I was under the impression that the balance would be shipped before I got back. I believe I told him that order was for 50 machines.

He said, "Now you get right busy and telegraph the Detroit factory instructions not to make any further shipments on the order, and notify Blessing that you have discovered defects in the machine of such a nature that you have decided to discontinue shipping for the present;" and with that, I called Patterson's attention to the fact that I had a letter on file in my office in which Blessing stated the Weiler and Detroit were the only low priced registers that he had ever handled that fulfilled the requirements of a cash register; and with that fact made clear to Mr. Patterson, he got up and raised his hand and says, "The idea of Mr. Chalmers maintaining a plant in Detroit, manufac-turing a cash register in direct competition with our low priced machine, that is a cash register"; and he nearly broke the table in front of him with his fist. He says, "Go right back to Detroit; disman-tle that plant; put it on board cars and ship it to Dayton as quickly as possible"; which I did.[10]

Patterson's brilliance in conceiving new business methods is nowhere more aptly exemplified than by Samuel Crowther's descrip-tion of Patterson's self-developed communica-tion philosophy

At the [NCR sales] convention of 1886 he was trying to illustrate a point with his hands when it suddenly struck him that he could make his point the more clearly in school fashion with a black-board. He sent out for a blackboard and thereafter he never held a meeting without a blackboard on which to draw a diagram of what he was talking about. Out of this grew the whole theory of teach-ing through the eye . . . Describing it, he once said:

" . . . my whole system of business teaching; . . . 1. Teach through the eye. 2. Contrast the right with the wrong way. . . .

"Business is only a form of teaching. You teach people to desire your product; that is selling. You teach workmen how to make the right product; that is manufacturing. You teach others to cooper-ate with you; that is organization. To succeed in business it is necessary to make the other man see things as you see them. I say 'as you see them'—which means that you yourself must first see and believe before you can tell another. . . .

"One of the many advantages of teaching through the eye is its exactness. . . . I have often heard a speaker ask, 'Do you see my point?' He wants to know if the hearer actually has the point in eye as well as mind, that he understands it well enough to make a mental picture. Well, then, why not draw the picture? Instead of asking if the point is seen, why not draw the point so that it cannot help being seen? . . .

"I have found that words, whether written or spoken, without some kind of drawing on which to center attention, are not effective.

The very first advertising that we put out after starting the N.C.R. taught me this lesson. I had some five thousand circulars printed describing the new machine and what it would do. I told what it had done for me and how it could prevent business leaks. It was a good circular but it did not contain a picture of the cash register. Having put the envelopes into the mails, we hurriedly hired two extra men to answer inquiries. We waited and we might be waiting still, for we did not get a single inquiry. Nobody knew what we were talking about! . . .

"Very few people understand words . . . 'Food' to a baby means milk . . . but 'food' to a chef calls up thousands of delicacies . . . as something primarily to prepare rather than something for himself to eat. . . .

"The ideal presentation of a subject is one in which every sub-division is pictured and the words are used only to connect them. . . .

"I early found that in dealing with men a picture was worth more than anything I could say. I used to employ an artist to hang around in the shops with me and quietly make sketches of things that were not being done right.

"Then the sketches were made into drawings and I called the men together and showed them exactly what they were doing. . . .

"Once when I found an audience of agents getting away from me, I held up a ten-dollar bill before them, tore it to bits, and threw it on the floor. The people sat up, and then I said:

"'Did you think I was going to waste that bill? I was only trying to show you what you were wasting by not giving attention!' Turning to an assistant, I continued: 'Just pick up the pieces of that bill and paste them together.'"[11]

These firsthand recollections give a fairly clear picture of Patterson as a strongly objective-driven person with great intuition, unafraid to use power to accomplish his goals. He had his own ideas of what was legal and fair— stemming from a strong belief that he had almost a divine right to a complete monopoly on the cash register business.

John H. Patterson was smart, resourceful, quick acting . . . and ruthless. The results are history.

Part Two

Collector Information on Early Registers

[7]

The Early Woodies of NCR

All National Manufacturing and all early NCR machines built before 1887 were encased in wood. An attempt to collect representative samples of the wood machines going all the way back to the Ritty registers is conceivable, but it would be very difficult. The early "deep drawer" NCR's, any of the National Manufacturing machines (1882-84) and certainly any Ritty register (1879-1881), sets apart the advanced collection. Between the Ritty and National Manufacturing registers, there were perhaps 1,000 shipped in total, of which one might expect only

about 1% (10 registers) to have survived today. That there are six Ritty and 15 to 20 National Manufacturing machines which are known to exist is attributed to the practice of NCR itself to have warehoused large numbers of obsolete machines.

The National Manufacturing machines had

Fig. 7-1: Saloon photo reproduced from the July, 1890 (No. 45) issue of *The Hustler*, NCR's house magazine. Note the 30-key wood shallow-drawer register typical of the 1897-1890 period. It has a rail, rectangular pull and metal top sign. The saloon is the interior of the Metropolitan Hotel Bar, George Street, Sydney, Australia.

THE FAMOUS BAR-MAIDS OF AUSTRALIA.

Fig. 7-2: The first National Manufacturing case style
housing a paper-punch mechanism with no cash drawer.
The spindle gallery was the most impressive design feature
of all the National Manufacturing case designs. Photo
reproduced from Samuel Crowther's book, *John Patterson,
Pioneer in Industrial Welfare*.

Fig. 7-3: National Manufacturing 24-key paper-punch register without cash drawer. This machine, encased in walnut,
shows the early scalloped indicators and the round tag
identifying it as number 6 sample in the NCR model room.
That indicates an early register, perhaps 1882 or early 1883.
Tom Kunkel collection.

many variations, but they have a family look about them. They all look somewhat primitive, high-backed with simple case decorations consisting of turned spindles or some grooved stripes, geometric patterns and burled panels. Cases for both the Ritty Brothers and National Manufacturing were built by outside cabinet maker(s).

A study of extant machines produces an approximate chronology of early case designs and features. There is no known catalog of National Manufacturing or early NCR models. Also, the progression of early serial numbers is murky, but some approximate sense can be made from practical observations.

The First National Manufacturing Registers

The very first National Manufacturing machines had design features that may have carried over from the last Ritty detail adders and paper punch registers. In 1882, registers probably did not have cash drawers, although two of the earliest known National Manufacturing registers have identical cases, yet one has a cash drawer and the other doesn't. Both of these machines are unavailable for photography, but they are important enough to warrant some verbal description.

Morgan's Patent Safety Money Drawer.

This combination money drawer is made of the very best material, polished hardwood front (7-8 inch. thickness) a hardwood sliding till with six compartments for denominations of silver inclusive of four divisions for currency. Cannot be opened without knowing the combination. The bell will give the alarm. Perfect safety and indispensable for the trade. No springs or screws used. Lock first class. Regular size: 15x18x5 inches.

Our Price, $1.75 each.

...The Universal Cash Register...

Patented May 1st, 1894, United States of America and Europe.   PRICE, $1.50.

Delivered to any part in the U. S.   Charges prepaid.

Made to fit the ordinary Cash Drawer, length 9½ inches, depth 5 inches.   Can be laid flat or set at the two angles as shown by the short and long legs, enabling you more readily to make change, holding over $90 worth of coin.   The Registering Plates are to count New and Worn coin as commercially received and paid out. Wonderful. Useful. Compact. Ornament. Simple. Convenient.

Fig. 7-4a, b: A typical money drawer and insert that fits under the counter. This ad is from an 1898 Nafew (New York) catalogue. (Rick Crandall collection)

Fig. 7-5a: Drawer interior of deep-drawer machine. The change tray slides back and forth exposing bill trays below. Paper roll in rear of drawer is in storage. This drawer is from the register shown in Figures 7-19 and 20.

Figure 7-2. The spindle-top gallery is very attractive and distinctive. In the figure, the lid is raised blocking a view of the indication and the identification tags. Although there are differences, the register in Figure 7-3 does show the appropriate indication with scalloped tabs and identifying signage. On top of the indicator glass is a sign saying "Cash RegisteR" and the metal tag under the indicator glass identifies the National Manufacturing Co. of Dayton, Ohio.

The key checks (surfaces) are nickel silver, a carry-over from the Ritty machines. The lid is slanted and inset. In addition, there is a spindle on either side of the indicator glass, an embellishment that was continued in other models (see Figure 7-10 for example). These features (the slant front, spindles, etc.) appear to be unique to National Manufacturing although it is possible they were in design by Ritty.

The model with drawer is identical in appearance except that it is even more impressive. The entire register sits atop a deep cash drawer in an integrated cabinet. The drawer front has a

simple curved finger grip for a drawer pull identical to the pull shown in Figure 7-11a. On the almost-nonexistent till shelf (the drawer extended very little beyond the register in closed position), the register has a metal railing with a twisted rope design.

The Deep Drawer

The so-called "deep drawer" was designed to accommodate a sliding change tray that was stacked on top of the bill trays. This format derived from the pre-mechanical cash tills that had identical sliding change trays as shown in Figure 7-4. In fact, if you find a cash till, the sliding tray will fit perfectly in a 30-key size deep-drawer National.

This drawer width was one of the early standards causing a popular register width to be 19″. The standard arose from the arrangement of four side-by-side bill receptacles, one each for singles, fives, tens and twenties.

Figs. 7-5b, c: The cash drawer from the register in Figure 7-21. The rectangular sliding coin tray was originally in the drawer. The round bin tray is from an under counter cash till purchased at an antique market. It fits perfectly! Rick Crandall collection.

The Second National: A Simpler Design

The next model had the spindle gallery eliminated, but retained the simpler geometric carved molding across the top. This made the register several inches shorter. Extant models of this design have a shallow drawer with two added ring pulls flanking the centered finger pull. See Figure 7-8 for a sample of the ring pulls.

The identification plaques, slant lid and other details were preserved. Machines of this design are likely in the 750-1000 serial number range. Several are known to exist.

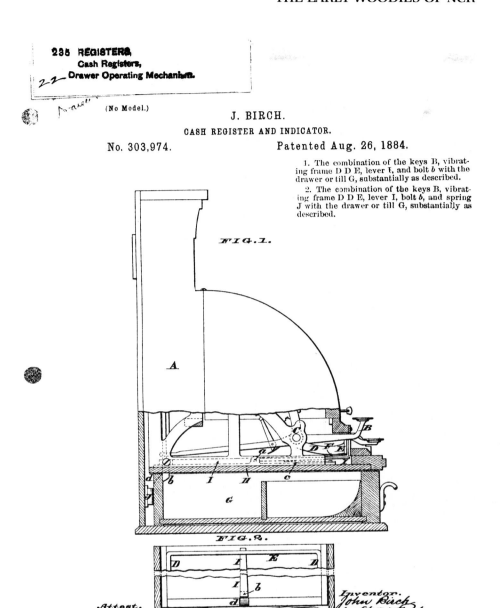

(No Model.)

J. BIRCH.
CASH REGISTER AND INDICATOR.

No. 303,974.   Patented Aug. 26, 1884.

1. The combination of the keys B, vibrating frame D D E, lever I, and bolt *b* with the drawer or till G, substantially as described.

2. The combination of the keys B, vibrating frame D D E, lever I, bolt *b*, and spring J with the drawer or till G, substantially as described.

FIG.1.

FIG.2.

Attest.   Inventor.
E. W. ...   John Birch
...   by ... & ...
                                his attys.

Fig. 7-7: Birch patent granted in August, 1884 for an improved locking cash drawer. Note the curved lid design and the hooked finger pull on the drawer. This appears to be nearly identical to the registers in Figures 7-6 and 7-11a.

Fig. 7-6: This Model 1 1/2 detail adder, probably produced in early 1884, is in original condition. Indication was viewed only from the front, typical of a bar register. The top gallery is indicative of middle-period National Manufacturing styling. Information under the drawer indicates that while the machine had seen commercial service, it was also used in an exhibit by NCR in an East Coast lawsuit—undoubtedly explaining its preservation. Al Levinson collection.

The Curved Lid Appears

The next case change likely occurred in 1884, no later than the spring. This design abandoned the slant lid in favor of a curved lid that would remain a standard at National for years to come. An example in small machine format is shown in Figure 7-6. This style is contemplated in the Birch patent shown in Figure 7-7, which was issued in August, 1884. These machines had a crest in a few different styles, but all similar to the crest on the machine in Figure 7-6.

Figs. 7-8, 9: National Model 2, 25-key deep-drawer register with the crenelated top gallery characteristic of late 1884 National Manufacturing cases. This machine is serial #A1270 (the "A" indicates that the sale was made by an agent rather than National itself). The patent tag says "The National Cash Register Company, Pat'd November 4, '79; Jan. 30, '83." This was one of the very early NCR machines built while National Manufacturing was still in existence and then sold under NCR's name in early 1885. Jimmy Filler collection.

The center finger-loop pull was eliminated on the wider machines, leaving the two ring pulls on the drawer front. The wider registers also returned to the deep-drawer arrangement which continued on into NCR's early models up to 1887 when shallow drawers returned permanently.

The rope design on the railing was also temporarily abandoned in favor of a plain railing.

The Final National Manufacturing Style

A final style change at National Manufacturing was made sometime between summer and fall of 1884. The differences were small but noticeable. A crenelated top gallery was introduced as depicted in Figure 7-8. Over a half dozen of these registers are known today, most of which have early NCR tags above the indicator glass (see Figure 7-10). This indicates that when NCR was formed, the existing supply of cases were used up. They became the earliest NCR machines in early 1885.

These registers had some extra detailing on the sides in the form of some geometric carving.

Patterson's NCR

On December 27, 1884, immediately after Patterson took over as president, he changed the National Manufacturing name back to the National Cash Register Co. Serial numbers in December, 1884, were in the 1150-1350 area, although only 24 registers were shipped that month.

Patterson worked quickly and effectively, rising from his humble beginnings in late 1884. He customized the selection of features in order to get sales; anything the customer wanted was okay with him. Adding to the profusion of styles was the rapid progress of enhancement. He sought a better register tirelessly.

Five hundred registers were sold in all of 1885, Patterson's first full year of business. The most popular models of late 1884 were the No. 2 1/2 (20-key detail adder) and No. 3 1/2 (30-key detail adder). The smaller Model 1 was an eleven-key saloon register ringing from 5¢ to $1.00 and the 1 1/2 was the candy store variety ringing from 1¢ to 50¢.

In January of 1885, Patterson must have reorganized the model numbers from predominantly fractional numbers (2 1/2's and 3 1/2's) to predominantly whole numbers (2's and 3's) although the complete renumbering is not known precisely. Fractional numbers did reappear in the NCR line.

Patterson continued the practice of procuring cases from the outside. Some cases are stamped M. Ohmer & Sons, Dayton. Ohmer was an office furniture maker who made the NCR register cases at least into 1887. It is likely that Ohmer made some or all of the cases for the earlier National Manufacturing Company.

NCR's First Case Design

As shipments increased during 1885, some standardization began to stabilize case designs. By April, the National Manufacturing cases were

Fig. 7-10: NCR Model 2 1/2 (lowest key is 5¢) detail adder serial #1545, shipped April 7, 1885, to D. C. Ross in San Francisco. This is another late National Manufacturing deep-drawer machine in cherry case with simple carvings, nickel-silver key checks, two drawer pulls, plain rail and scalloped gallery. The indicator housing glass is bevelled. The register price was $175. Jimmy Filler collection.

exahusted and by the fall of 1885, the first somewhat standardized NCR designs were introduced, although the lid carvings were still customized either with customer names, initials or special patterns.

Carvings were a bit more elaborate on this case, particularly the diamond braid on the lid edges and the ray pattern carved on the lid sides. A long narrow patent plate appeared just above the lid, but at this stage no model number information was to be seen on the exterior of the case. The model number and shipment date and destination are shown on paper tags usually glued to the back of the drawer.

The railing design reverted back to the fancier twisted rope pattern. The drawer pulls were also changed from two rings to a single centered rectangular pull that became standard.

Key checks were still made of nickel silver. Woods used were cherry, walnut, mahogany and occasionally oak and maple on the very early machines with walnut and mahogany being an increasingly popular choice all through the 1880's and early 1890's. Oak and mahogany became the popular woods towards 1900.

Salesman's Samples

All through the 1880's, Patterson had many problems to overcome, not the least of which was resistance and obstruction by store clerks themselves. Whether clerks and sales people didn't want a good thing to end or whether they just didn't like the intimation that a cash register on the premises indicated lack of trust on the proprietor's part, the result was the same. They threw out direct mail pieces before they got to the store owner, they prevented cash register salesmen from entering the premises and, in some cases, they would boycott an establishment that put a register on trial.[1]

NCR salesmen resorted to remaining anonymous in order to gain entry. Instead of carrying a register, they brought a salesman's sample mechanism hidden in small wood cases. Once gaining audience with the proprietor, the sample would be demonstrated in private.

The First "High Style" NCR Case Design

The first standard inlay design appeared in early 1886. Registers still sported deep drawers, but now with more refined raised square panels around the base and cash drawer and a well-executed inlay pattern of honeysuckle flowers bordering the lid and a leafy design on the side. The patent plate, drawer pull, key check and railing continued similarly to the earlier carved case.

The inlaid honeysuckle lid design continued for three or four years, at least until 1889. Brass was used increasingly as an inlay material to great effect. One of the most beautiful wood machines ever made was the honeysuckle inlay pattern enhanced with brass inlaid beading outlining the drawer panels, and burled walnut used for the insets.

The mechanisms of these machines made slow progress. The first detail-adder wheels were enumerated identically with sequential numbers that merely told the proprietor the number of presses for each day. It was up to the proprietor to multiply the number of key presses times the key value and then sum across all keys to get a cumulative cash total for the day. This, of course, would be checked against the cash drawer contents to discover theft. The first adder wheels were made of nickel silver with stamped numbers.

Sometime in early 1886, Patterson purchased a simple adding mechanism that allowed each key transaction to be accumulated in dollars and cents instead of the number of key presses, thus eliminating one manual arithmetic step. Adder wheels quickly evolved to paper coverings with printed numbers, resulting in the classic detail adder that would last until 1912 or so.

The German silver key checks were replaced by glass key checks contained by round metal key hoops. The earliest known machine with glass key checks and dollar value adder wheels was shipped on July 27, 1886 shown in Figure 7-22.

In 1886, a total of 1,050 registers were shipped, double the figure of a year earlier. The figure would double again to 1,995 machines in 1887.

Fig. 7-11a, b: This Model 1 1/2 detail adder was produced probably late in 1884 since there is no top crest. The indicators can be seen from the front and rear. The NCR name tag indicates a reissue which indeed occurred in 1886, at which time it would have been renumbered a Model 1. The crotch maple lid inset was part of the restoration of the machine. Key tops are nickel silver. Jimmy Filler collection.

Ohmer Letter File Cabinets.

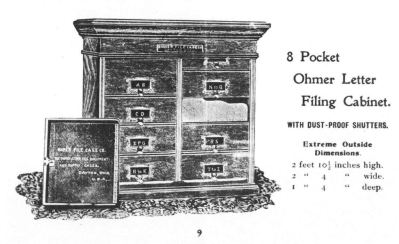

8 Pocket
Ohmer Letter
Filing Cabinet.

WITH DUST-PROOF SHUTTERS.

Extreme Outside Dimensions.

2 feet 10½ inches high.
2 " 4 " wide.
1 " 4 " deep.

9

Fig. 7-12 An early catalog insertion showing a wood business furniture product of Ohmer Co., Dayton, Ohio.

Ohmer made many of the early wood cases for National Manufacturing and NCR (and perhaps Ritty as well).

Fig. 7-13: NCR Model No. 3, 30-key deep-drawer detail adder, serial #A1672, originally shipped on June 18, 1885. It has the plain railing, nickel-silver key checks, double drawer pulls and simple carvings on the side. The patent tag is above the indicator window. This was probably the first design created by NCR. Side carvings of this type show up on other extant machines. Jimmy Filler collection.

Fig. 7-14a, b: NCR Model No. 3, 30-key deep-drawer detail adder, serial #1881. The lid carving of a Solomon's-seal wildflower is probably a customization although the rest of the case decoration follows an increasingly standard design. Here we see the switch to a single rectangular drawer pull used until 1889-90 when the Patterson Pull became standard. This register has unusual key values; note the $1.75 indication. The patent plate has moved under the indicator glass where it stayed in future models. Still no top sign. Jimmy Filler collection.

Figs. 7-15, 16: NCR Model 3 1/2 (lowest key is 1¢)
deep-drawer detail adder, serial #2031 shipped on December 8, 1885, to Hill & Brundage in Russell, Kansas, price
$100. H&B is custom carved on the lid, although side
carvings comply with the standard. The case is walnut and
the railing is now back to a rope design. Jimmy Filler
collection.

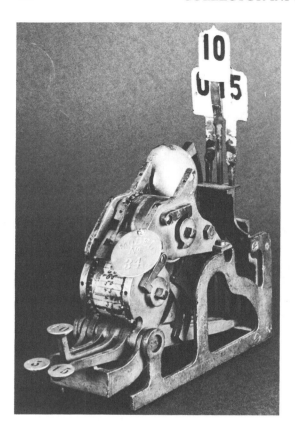

Fig. 7-17a: NCR salesman's sample of the detail-adder mechanism used in early deep-drawer machines. Note the nickel-silver key checks. This extant model is rare and includes carrying case and an NCR model tag (#36) indicating this particular item was kept in NCR's model room for a period of its life. Rick Crandall collection.

Fig. 7-17b: A photo reproduced from Crowther's *John Patterson, A Pioneer in Industrial Welfare* showing the identical salesman's sample in use.

THE "THREE KEY SAMPLE"

When clerks and bartenders organized to oppose the introduction of cash registers, the agents found it almost impossible to reach proprietors of stores with their big machines. Mr. Patterson met this objection by making a small working model of the register, enclosed in a leather case with no marks on the outside to identify it with the N. C. R. Co.

Fig. 7-18: NCR Model 3 deep-drawer detail adder, serial #2409 shipped on April 20, 1886, to Wagner in Winona, Minnesota. This is one of the first uses of the standard honeysuckle inlay pattern, combined with two vertical trees in this and one other known example. The walnut case has applied panels around the base and drawer front. Scott Anixter collection.

Fig. 7-19: NCR paper-punch version of the No. 3 1/2 with deep drawer and unique inlay design of birds and flowers. The serial number is #2568, shipped on June 30, 1886, to L. Mathew in Chicago. The brass-framed glass top sign is added, but is one of the styles appropriate to the register. Scott Anixter collection.

Fig. 7-20: NCR Serial #2568 showing the paper roll under the lid. A punch is made in the appropriate scribed column every time a key is pressed. The holes are counted and multiplied by the key values at the end of each day.

Figs. 7-21, 22a, b: NCR Model 3 deep-drawer detail adder with honeysuckle wood and brass inlay pattern. The serial is #2644, shipped on July 27, 1886, to C. F. Kline of Dayton, Ohio. This high-styled case also has circular brass dots inlaid around the burled walnut panels on the drawer and burled walnut lid insert— one of the most beautiful of all the wood designs. Five or six are known indicating high original popularity for such an early machine. This particular register employs the earliest-known use of glass key checks which then became a new standard on high-grade machines. The top sign shown in fig. 7-21 is added although authentic to the register. It has a cast pattern that replicates the design on the side of the lid.

The crank shown in fig. 7-22b is the only one known for a deep-drawer machine. It is used to reset the counters to zero. Rick Crandall collection.

The register of 1886 was very different from the 1884 machines. Cosmetically, everything was different. Earlier indicators were made of unpainted tin with stencilled numbers; amounts could be seen only a few feet away from the register. Patterson had one of his developers (C. W. Stewart) experiment with better indicators and soon they had a white indicator tab with heavy black figures that could be seen 20 feet away.

The 1885 and 1886 models had no "Change" key, so usually the storekeeper would designate the highest value key as a null key used just to open the drawer and to be ignored in totalling money amounts. This was certainly done by the storekeeper. Then a special key was added labelled "Change" for this purpose. As the story goes, when a customer handed in a quarter for a 15¢ purchase, the clerk pushed the "Change" key instead of properly registering 15¢. Then he would return 10¢ "Change" to the customer and pocket the 15¢. The customers were not sufficiently familiar with the register to know that "Change" did not mean that they were supposed to get change back from a real transaction.

When Patterson heard of this wrinkle, he abolished the "Change" key and put in its place a "Nothing Sold" key and indicator and then a "No Sale" key and indicator that could not be misunderstood.

In 1887, there were five models: two paper-roll machines and three detail adders. The Model 3, 30-key detail adder was considered the biggest seller of them all—perhaps the most likely to appear today.

In late 1886, the change to shallower cash drawers occurred, just before the introduction of metal cases. The first known shallow-drawer wider machine is a Model 2 wood machine with the Honeysuckle inlay pattern in the John Apple collection. It is serial #2888 shipped on October 15, 1886. At least one example of a deep-drawer machine in a scroll-design bronze case is known. Use of wood cases as an option continued into the early 1900's.

Glass key checks continued as did rope-design railing, rectangular pull and long patent plate above the lid. A new standard inlay design emerged called "Lily of the Valley." Either

Fig. 7-23: The only available photo of the scroll-design bronze-cased deep-drawer register with 20 keys. The Patterson pull indicates a late (1889) deep-drawer register.

Fig. 7-24: Model 2, 25-key deep-drawer detail adder. This is the latest deep drawer that has appeared to date. It has cash counters for each key position instead of the older key press counters. The top sign has been added. The knob on the upper left side is a bell silencer—a standard feature then. There is also a special "Charge" key.

Figs. 7-25, 26: NCR Model 3 shallow-drawer paper-punch machine with honeysuckle inlay design. This was one of the early shallow-drawer registers (serial #3716), shipped on May 4, 1887. The case was made by Ohmer & Sons. Jimmy Filler collection.

Fig. 7-27: NCR Model 2, 25-key shallow-drawer paper-punch machine in "Lily of the Valley" inlay plus a customized lid monogram. The initials are "H & C," standing for Hopkins and Cahn of Appleton, Wisconsin. Serial #3745, shipped May 6, 1887.

Fig. 7-28: Model 2 with lid raised and paper punch
exposed.

Fig. 7-29: Model 3 standard shallow-drawer machine circa 1889. The lid has a customized name added: "Contra Costa."

Fig. 7-30: NCR Model 3 detail-adder shallow-drawer register in walnut case with honeysuckle lid inlay. Serial #9748, shipped on February 5, 1889, to Verstine & Sandl in Brookville, PA. Sam Robins collection.

Fig. 7-31: Model 3 detail-adder shallow-drawer with
standard "Lily of the Valley" inlay design.

Fig. 7-32: NCR Model 3, 30-key register with elongated drawer front. Serial #10,082, shipped on February 26, 1889, to T. M. Jones & Co. The bigger drawer was for greater capacity and was also available in metal cases. Tom Kunkel collection.

Fig. 7-33: NCR Model 2, shallow-drawer register with the new standard clamshell inlay design. The Patterson pull is now evident on the drawer front and the rail is still present.

Fig. 7-34: NCR Model 4, clamshell inlay design with customized lid sign for "H. G. Thompson." Note the multiple $.15 indicators demonstrating that this register is really multiple registers in one departmentalized machine as shown in the next photo. Jimmy Filler collection.

Fig. 7-35: Same Model 4 with lid raised. Divided key bank is shown set up for a pharmacy with a separate set of keys just for prescriptions, etc. The Model 4 was usually selected for compartmentalization since it was the widest machine of the day.

it or the earlier Honeysuckle could be selected from mid-1887 to 1889.

In 1889, the "clamshell" inlay pattern made its debut. The clamshell design endured possibly due to the fact that wood cases were becoming less frequently chosen options at this point and were not receiving sufficient attention to encourage continuing design changes. The clamshell design uses brass and wood inlay material and is a very attractive symmetrical pattern. On light oak registers, the clamshell inlay material is black ebony which makes for a striking register.

Today in most collectible fields, anything in fancy cast brass or bronze is usually the most desirable, but with cash registers, early wood cases are the mark of an historically important and rare machine. To the serious collector, an attractive deep drawer is an essential corner-stone. A National Manufacturing machine sets a collection completely apart, whereas a Ritty would be the ultimate in rarity and historical importance.

[8]

The Kruse Check and Adding Machine Co.
New York

In 1885, the Kruse Check and Adding Machine Company was in business producing check-printing machines and other kinds of mechanized office equipment. During that year, NCR's registers were making their first impact on the national scene. Kruse was the first to put out a competitive register, and a total adder at that. Kruse also introduced a metal case when NCR was still using wood.

Charles Kruse, president, was interested in making rapid entry into the cash register business. He initiated at least two efforts to obtain register designs that would avoid infringement of existing patents. NCR was using press-down key registers exclusively and so Kruse became interested in a lever-operated principle. He made an arrangement with George Juengst & Sons, a firm engaged in the manufacture of machinists' tools at Croton Falls in Westchester County, New York, to produce a lever-operated machine as fast as possible. Kruse furnished no plans or specifications— only that it was to be a lever-operated machine.

In the meantime, Kruse initiated another project internally in his own company, which resulted in a simple, effective total-adding register with an upright round face and keys placed in a circle similar to a clock face. This "dial" machine was small, very good looking and effectively made. It operated by pressing the appropriate keys and pushing down on a handle on the right side of the machine.

A small indicator window at 12 o'clock on the dial face displayed the amount. This machine was probably in production as Kruse's first register. In fact, Kruse may not have ever had another commercial register style, because when the Juengst firm delivered a viable lever-operated machine in July, 1886, Charles Kruse paid for the development and shelved it without even encouraging patent application.

Eventually, after Lamson purchased Kruse's cash register assets, Charles Juengst was encouraged to file a patent application on the lever register, which he did successfully. It was this invention that resulted in the Lamson lever machine discussed in the Lamson section.

Meanwhile, the dial total adder achieved success in the market, particularly in the Eastern United States. National knocked out many Kruse dials, and today the machine is rare. Only a half dozen are known to exist.

In 1889, the Lamson Consolidated Store Service Company of New Jersey acquired certain cash register assets from Kruse. It is not clear if the dial machine was included in the purchase, although it is likely that it was. Kruse must have kept something of value in the cash register field, because when National eventually purchased Lamson's cash register business in March of 1893, it also paid Kruse $25,000 for certain assets.

The very next month after the double purchase, National wasted no time in putting out a flyer advertising its expanded line. The

Fig. 8-1: Early Kruse ad showing both a single dial and a triple-dial machine unknown today. The top sign on the triple dial resembles the top sign on the NCR deep-drawer detail adders of the same period. Note the emphasis on the total adder.

Control Your Cash and You Control Your Business.

AT LAST.

THE ✦ KING ✦ OF ✦ ALL ✦ REGISTERS.

The Best!
The Simplest!

THE CHEAPEST IN THE WORLD.

The Most Durable!
The Most Practical!

THAT IS WHAT THE

KRUSE ❀ CASH ❀ REGISTER ❀ COMPANY

OFFERS TO YOU.

THE ONLY CORRECT SYSTEMS

STYLE No. 1.

Adapted for
Wine Rooms, Restaurants, Soda Water Stands
&c., &c.

PRICE, $85.00.

STYLE No. 2.

These Machines are used in
Groceries, Butchers, Bakers, Boot and Shoes,
Confectionery, Drugs, Hardware, and
General Stores, or in any establishment
where sales are made from 1 cent up to $10.

PRICE, $100.00.

A DISCOUNT OF $10.00 ALLOWED FOR CASH.

What × Our × Machines × Will × Do!

They Add Total.
You have the amount of each day, month
and year's business for reference.
It Unlocks Cash Drawer.
It Requires no winding up.

It Shows the amount of Purchase.
It Can be used with or without Cashier.
In either way it gives perfect control of sale
It is the easiest to operate.
No chance for clerks to make errors.

And above all, it has the TOTAL ADDER, the most essential part in the Cash Register.

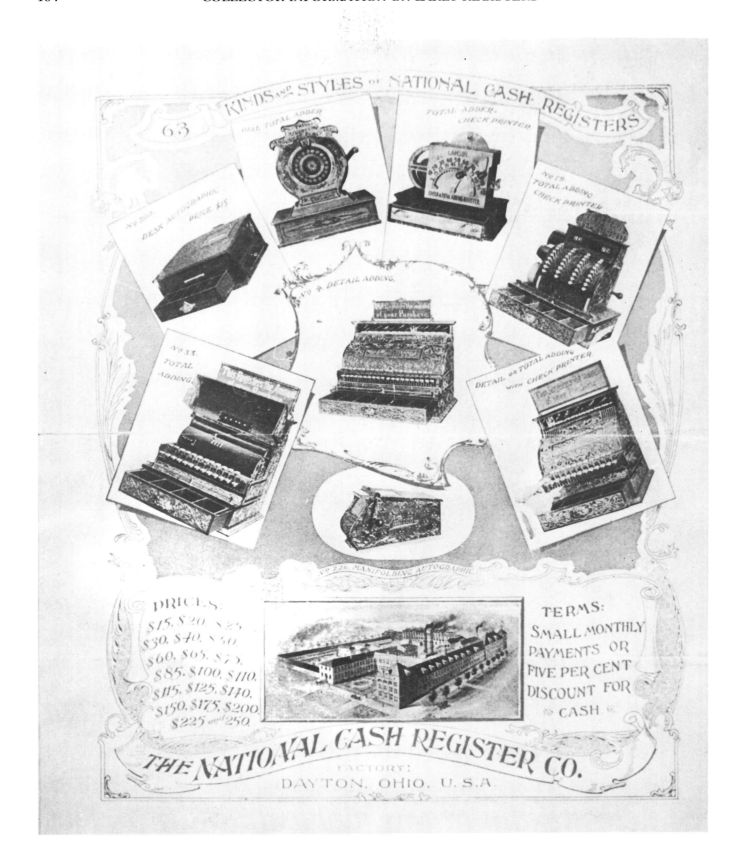

Fig. 8-2: 1893 NCR magazine ad showing a mixture of National, Kruse and Lamson machines in its expanded line. The dial is still identical to the Kruse decoration.

Fig. 8-3: Extant NCR knocker dial. This machine is located at NCR and was used as a photo prop for a *Business Week* article on NCR, May 5, 1987, page 110. Courtesy of *Business Week* and Bill Waugh, photographer.

Fig. 8-4: Extant example of a Kruse dial distributed by
Dreyfus & Co. The case is white painted enamel with gold
artwork. Rick Crandall collection.

Fig. 8-5: Rear view. Note that the lock itself is a collectible. It is a Scandinavian or "Scando" lock that was available contemporaneously with the Kruse.

April, 1893, flyer depicted eight machines, each of a unique type. One of these was the Kruse dial with the following description:

Total Adder, Single Dial
Indicates and registers from 5¢ to $1.00. Shows the total amount of the day's business. Used in small Cigar Stores, Soda Water Fountains, Restaurants, etc.[1]

Interestingly, National did have its own knocker version of the Kruse dial waiting in the wings since the previous December (1892). It is likely that National used their version of the dial as part of its persuasion to buy out Kruse and Lamson. The NCR version of the dial did, in fact, make it to market, but it remained in the line only for the rest of 1893. It was listed as the No. 110 principle of operation.

There are a number of variations of the Kruse dial machine. Indeed, just about every extant machine is different in some way. One type of Kruse dial has a mirror front with numbers etched around the face, clock style.

Another even more attractive variant is shown in Figures 8-4 to 8-6. This model was probably the standard since it is pictured as the machine in inventory that National obliged itself to sell after it acquired Kruse. It sports a white enamel cast-metal case with gold pinstriping and a leafy wreath pattern on the face. The cut-glass mirror and bronze top sign and drawer front make it a gleaming jewel.

The dial that NCR originally made as a knocker had a different mechanism with the crank in the middle of the clock face. Undoubtedly, this was an effort to avoid patent infringement. The striking cosmetic difference was the application of the cupid-and-moon casting on the left front of the face.

When National acquired Kruse along with Lamson, the inventory of Kruse dials were dressed up for sale by adding brass covers and rear plate, nickel plating the front face and applying the cupid casting and a National drawer front, all ideas from the knocker machine. The Kruse top sign was retained.

In any form, the Kruse dial is attractive, rare and historically important as the first NCR

TOTAL‑ADDER—Single‑Dial.

Indicates and registers amounts from 5c. to $1.00. Shows the total amount of the day's business. Operated by pressing in the proper button and pressing down the lever. Used in small Cigar Stores, Soda Water Fountains, Restaurants, etc.

Fig. 8-6: Kruse dial as pictured in an NCR circular before NCR changed the decoration.

competitor and the first commercial total adder since the Incorruptible Cashier.

More information can be found on the NCR dial machine in Volume II under the NCR 110 principle.

Fig. 8-7a: Here is a knocker ad from NCR circa 1892. The machine shown is unknown today (what a find this would be!). It is a Kruse double dial with center crank and tape printer. These ads bear out the fact that National actually had to take its knocker into the market to intimidate Kruse.

DON'T PAY $145 FOR THIS REGISTER.

The Kruse Two=Dial Cash Register,

TOTAL-ADDER WITH TAPE PRINTER,

Price, $145.

MANUFACTURED BY

The Kruse Cash Register Co.,

Indicates and registers amounts from 5c. to $19.95, and prints the amount of each registration on a strip of paper. The cabinet is of cast iron, enameled in white.

OF NEW YORK, N. Y.

Disadvantages of the Kruse Two-Dial Cash Register.

1. Nearly all of the wheels, and many of the other parts, are made in rough molds and of soft metal; and, as they will wear out easily, they cannot be as accurate as hard metal milled parts.

2. The title of this machine is not perfect, as it has two suits for infringement pending against it. One was instituted on March 19, 1892, against the Kruse Cash Register Company, and the other on August 17, 1892, against the same Company.

3. If the metal bar across the top of the register, under the indicators, is pressed in when a sale is being registered, no amount will be recorded or indicated.

4. When the cent adding wheels are at 95 cents, a sharp blow on the crank to the right, will make the adding wheels overthrow $1.00.

5. Access may be had to the cash drawer, at any time, by moving the crank until it is on a level with the $10.00 button, and then giving it a sharp rap in the reverse direction. This will cause the cash drawer to fly open without registering any amount.

WARNING: We have sued the manufacturers, also a number of users, of the Kruse Cash Register, for infringement of our patents, and we hereby warn all intending purchasers of the Kruse Cash Register of this fact. The Supreme Court of the United States holds that "It is infringement to use though made by another," and that "Innocent use is none the less infringement."

WHEN YOU CAN BUY THIS ONE FOR $100.

The National Two=Dial Cash Register,

TOTAL = ADDER WITH TAPE PRINTER,

Price, $100.

MANUFACTURED BY

The National Cash Register Co.,

Indicates and registers amounts from 5c. to $19.95, and prints the amount of each registration on a strip of paper. The cabinet is of cast iron, enameled in white.

OF DAYTON, OHIO.

Advantages of the National Cash Register Over the Kruse.

1. All of the wheels and other parts, are of hard metal, and milled instead of cast, thus insuring great hardness, making them less liable to wear out, and securing absolute accuracy. The works are stronger than the Kruse and will not so easily get out of order.

2. There are no infringement suits against it. Purchasers of this machine need have no fear of being sued for infringement.

3. There are no metal bars or other unnecessary parts on the front of the register, and it always registers the correct amount.

4. The adding wheels cannot be made to overthrow, but always add correctly and expose the right amounts.

5. It is necessary to press in a key to open the cash drawer. It cannot be opened by hitting a crank or by any similar operation.

A sale cannot be indicated in the opening at the top of the register, without registering the amount on the adding wheels, as this machine registers the amount at the time it indicates it.

We guarantee this machine to be superior in every respect to the Kruse Cash Register shown on the opposite page. It is much more ornamental and more easily operated, is more accurate and much more substantially made, besides being $45.00 less in price. Before ordering a Kruse or any other Cash Register of its class, examine this machine.

EXCHANGES: If you have a Kruse Cash Register, an old style National, or a register of any other make, and wish to exchange it for a New Improved National, write to us or any of our agencies. We make liberal terms on such exchanges.

Fig. 8-7b: The National knocker uses the fine scroll design and a double cupid. Competition from Patterson was ruthless.

Fig. 8-8: NCR's facelift of the dial. Note the National drawer front, the cupid casting and the nickel plating that replaced the white enamel.

Fig. 8- 9: The doors are bronze as is the rear cover plate.

[9]

The Boston Cash Indicator and Recorder Co.
The Boston Cash Register Co.
Northampton, Massachusetts

The Boston Cash Indicator and Recorder Co. jumped into the competitive fray soon after Kruse. Boston was formed on September 3, 1886, with James H. Wright as president. Jerome J. Webster of Somerville, Massachusetts, was the primary inventor and also the manager of manufacturing. Sometime in early 1890 the Boston Cash Register Company of 32 Masonic St., Northampton, Massachusetts, was formed to purchase the remains of the earlier Boston company. The purchase was completed on April 5, 1891.

The flagship Boston registers were total adders—joining with Kruse to spell the impending demise of the detail adder. Only three Bostons are known to exist today, two small No. 1 eleven-key machines in brass cases, and one larger No. 3 register in a wood case that has yielded much of the information about extended Boston features. There is indication in Boston's 1892 trademark application that Great Britain was the principal foreign market for this machine.

The discovery of the Boston "Number 3 Bank Machine" substantially enriched our knowledge of how far Boston went with its product line. One of the unusual aspects of the larger Boston is the way in which it achieves total adding. Boston seems to have studied the Ritty Incorruptible Cashier and set its target on an improved watch-cog type of adder. The counter wheels are enumerated on their faces rather than the more popular approach of stamping the edges of the wheels.

The disadvantage of Ritty and Boston-type adder wheels is the limited capacity for high ring-ups. Either the counter wheels had to get very large or their numerals had to get smaller as ring-ups increased. Boston solved the problem by subdividing the adding task to multiple sets of adders. The result is an impressive array of counters although the proprietor has to do the adding across the subsets of adders.

The Model 3 shows many design similarities to early NCR machines. Quality and design of the wood case is comparable to the simple carving on early NCR deep drawers before inlay patterns were used. The rope railing, the customized lid with proprietor's name, the "devil's-head" drawer pull and even the patent tag all create an NCR-like appearance.

The mechanism is solidly built and reliability was stressed by Boston. The register came with a two-year guarantee and a certification that it had been tested 1,000 times before it left the factory!

Another feature found on some Boston models was a two-level pair of change and bill drawers similar to the Chicago. Depressing the keys would cause a cover to recede, exposing a fixed-position coin drawer. If bills were needed, a catch in the coin drawer released the bill drawer which popped out in more traditional NCR style.

Bensinger patents on a similar money tray explained the purpose in terms of avoiding the difficulty of non-uniform spring ejection of a drawer that had to cope with a wide variance of

Fig. 9-1.

coin weights. By keeping only the bills in the movable drawer, not much weight variation had to be accommodated by the drawer spring. Boston called this a "novelty owned by the company."

Boston models were

No. 1 Eleven-key total adder, one bank (usually 5¢ to 50¢) "specially adapted for soda fountains, dime lunches, bakeries, etc." Available in wood or metal cases. The top sign was quite fancy. Two metal versions of the register are known to exist today.

No. 2 Twenty-key total adder, two banks (usually 5¢ to $5). Wood encased with a glass top sign similar to the No. 3.

No. 3 Twenty-seven-key total adder, three banks (1¢ to $10) and rings to $11,000. This is the largest capacity register in the Boston line, "very desirable machine for retail groceries and other retail stores." The top sign is glass framed in a metal roping. Lid counter, special charge keys and counters and finger rail are among the extras on this register. The coin section of the drawer has a metal bottom with perforations to allow coin dust to fall through. One of these is known to exist.

No. 4 Twelve-key total adder, two banks (one bank had only two keys). This model had the fixed coin tray and moveable bill drawer arrangement. The top sign was very fancy with a carved lion on each side. None extant today.

No. 5 Twenty-one-key total adder, two banks. This model also had the fixed coin tray and moveable bill drawer and the same fancy top sign as the No. 4. This case came in wood and metal.

No. 6 Thirty-one-key total adder, three banks and $11,000 capacity. This register had the fixed coin tray and moveable bill drawer and fancy top sign. Encased in wood or metal.

No. 7 Thirty-key detail adder. This was a differently designed register with detail adders under a hinged cover that was the whole front of the register. This was Boston's entry into the low-priced market.

Boston's early entry was rewarded with NCR's first legal assault. In September 1888, NCR sued Boston and did so again in May, 1889, and March, 1891. The May, 1889 action was a patent infringement suit filed against Boston for using a patent that had been issued to John Patterson just twelve months earlier. The main object of the patent was to prevent key strokes while the cash drawer was open. This forced the clerk to close the drawer after each transaction so that he or she would have to use the keys to open the drawer for the next transaction. This was an important feature that made the register a more reliable check and balance.

Fig. 9-2: Boston Cash Register which rings to $.50. Top sign is not original; no authentic Boston top sign is known today. Jimmy Filler collection.

One section of Patterson's testimony in that suit indicates that he may have learned a thing or two from Boston, particularly about trading out and knocking out machines:

> I was not aware that the defendant was using the patented [#382,647 granted to Heady and Patterson] invention until last month, that is, April, 1889, at which time I came into possession of one of its machines and submitted it to my counsel, who, upon examination, informed me that it . . . was a direct infringement thereof, and I thereupon at once took steps to have suit brought against the defendant for such infringement.
>
> To my knowledge, the construction of a machine embodying these features by the defendant has enabled it to sell its machines and give satisfaction to purchasers when it otherwise could not have done so, . . . In the section of the country in which the defendant has operated, the sale of the complainant's machines from this cause has been largely demoralized, and in fact, almost suspended, . . .
>
> In this New England territory it has been the custom of the complainant to allow purchasers of its machines to pay for them in installments. . . . In a great number of instances, the defendant or its agents . . . have sought out that purchaser, have offered one of the defendant's machines at a very much less price than the price of complainant's machine, and have induced him to break his agreement with the complainant and return the machine which he had received from the complainant . . .[1]

So Boston was knocking out NCR registers in 1888!

A fierce legal battle was fought. Boston actually won the first round and obtained a dismissal of charges in October of 1893. Boston must have had startup problems that went beyond these legal thrusts as evidenced by the small production of machines. In the five-year period from September 3, 1886, to September 3, 1892, a total of 400 registers were sold. Then, in the one year from April, 1891, to April of 1892, 693 registers were sold. From these figures we can estimate that Boston's total life-time production was less than 3,000 machines.

While legal actions were pending, Boston's financial woes worsened and the company

Fig. 9-3: The other extant small Boston, also incomplete. This machine rings to $1.00. Jimmy Filler collection.

finally fell into the hands of new owners who attempted to revive it.

National's semi-monthly house organ, called the *N.C.R.*, proudly displayed an article that was carried in the Northampton (Mass.) *Daily Herald* on September 1, 1894. The *N.C.R.* said:

> Another Black Eye for the Old Boston Co.
>
> The property of the Boston Cash Register Company was sold yesterday under a foreclosure of mortgage to the mortgagees, about ten of the principal stockholders who had advanced $25,000 for available funds . . . the highest bid was $16,000.
>
> It is now planned to reorganize the company and proceed soon to the manufacture of machines . . .[2]

Patterson was stubborn and he insisted that the case be appealed to the U.S. Supreme Court. The highest court in the land accepted the case and overturned the lower court ruling:

Fig. 9-4: A complete Boston mechanism that served time in the NCR model room (Model 973). Perhaps this was a model used by NCR in its legal endeavors against Boston. Rick Crandall collection.

The earliest patent to which our attention is called, and which may be said to represent the infancy of the art, is that to James Russell, October 10, 1829 for an improvement in bell ringing.[3]

The Russell patent provided for a device intended for hotels where some means was desired for any room to alert the front desk. A box with a bell and indicators was designed to be located at the hotel front desk and when a wire from a particular room was pulled, the bell would ring and an indicator would pop up indicating the room. It would stay up until the next bell was rung.

Fig. 9-5: Boston Model 3 Bank Machine with 30 keys subdivided in three banks, each with its own total adder. This register, serial #3019, was shipped on March 5, 1894. Key checks are oval ceramic and ring from 1¢ to $10 plus special keys for "Change," "Pay Out" and a blank key used for "No Sale." The mahogany wood case with raised panels has provision for a top sign (missing). The patent tag shows a number of patents dated from 8/20/87 to 11/29/92. Rick Crandall collection.

Fig. 9-6: Under the lid of the Boston Model 3. Provision is made for quite a bit of counting. Three total-adding pairs of ceramic-coated counter wheels for the three banks, a counter for each special key, and an unusual lid counter housed under lock and key in a nickel-plated metal container on the lid. There is a lever for muffling the bell. A button with "A" stamped on it (for "arrester") has four functions depending on its position in relation to its associated lock: either the register is locked (i.e. no keying possible), unlocked, partially locked (requiring pressing the "A" button before each transaction), or just the blank key is locked. Internal parts are all substantial metal and nickel plated.

Fig. 9-7: Instructions found under the lid in use of features.

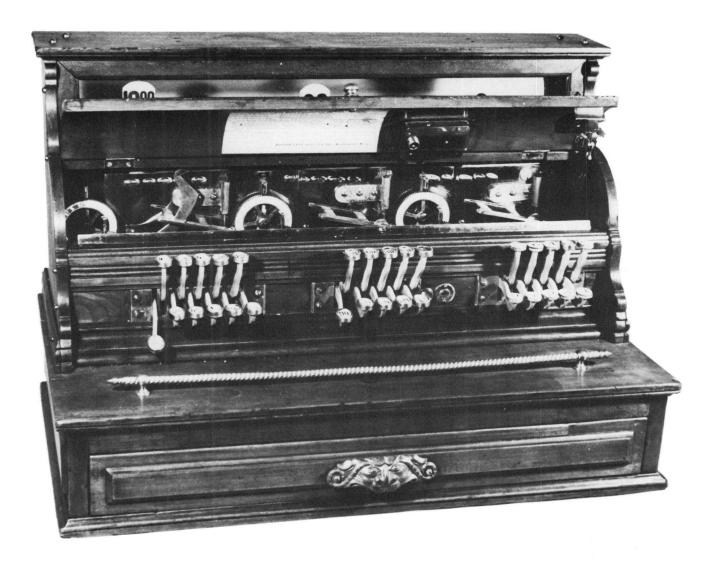

DIRECTIONS TO READ A NUMBER 3 BANK MACHINE.

Each Wheel is Provided with 100 Teeth.

On the RIGHT HAND set of wheels { Each tooth on the FRONT wheel represents 1c.
Each tooth on the BACK wheel represents $1.00.

On the CENTER set of wheels ...... { Each tooth on the FRONT wheel represents 10c.
Each tooth on the BACK wheel represents $10.00.

On the LEFT HAND set of wheels.... { Each tooth on the FRONT wheel represents $1.00.
Each tooth on the BACK wheel represents $100.00.

To set the Machine :-Turn all the front wheels to the left until their pointers stand on division lines next before 0; then turn the back wheels in the same way until their pointers also stand on division lines next before 0. Now push down the 1c key in the right hand bank, the 10c key in the middle bank and the $1.00 key in the left hand bank and the machine is set with all the pointers on 0. The push button A controls the operation of the keys, in three ways, viz. : Push back the button A and turn the lock key to the right and all of the keys are free to operate ; turn the lock key to the left and you will be obliged to press back the button A each time, before a key can be operated. To lock all keys and machine, depress the blank key and turn the lock key to the right.and all the keys and machine are completely locked.

To operate the keys when draw is open :-Push the lever located inside of Cabinet centre of machine in front to right ; to lock keys when draw is open, to left; necessitating shutting draw before each depression of key.

To lock the blank key independent of the others, pull forward the lever which is located over it inside of Cabinet ; to muffle the bell, push the short lever over the dials to the left.

To show the tags for dollars and fractions of a dollar : for example, $8.72, press down the 8 dollar key and 70 cent key, hold the 8 dollar key down until you have put down the 2 cent key, then let them return to place.

BOSTON CASH REGISTER CO., Northampton, Mass.

N. B. In registering *be sure to push down each key used to its fullest extent*, then it will return to its normal position by its own weight.

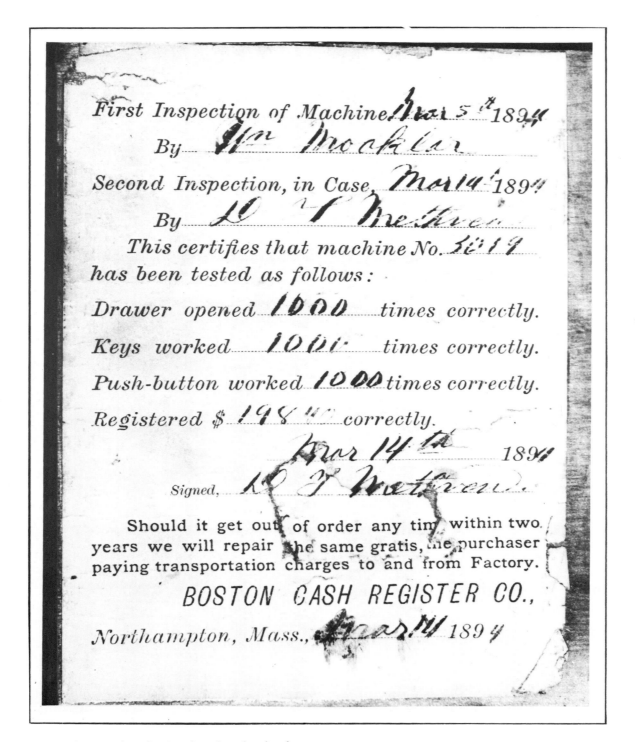

Fig. 9-8: Identification found under the drawer.

The Supreme Court found only one difference between that mechanism and the Ritty & Birch patent, namely the Ritty & Birch use of keys connected to the indicators. Other patents were reviewed by the Supreme Court and it concluded:

> To sum up the state of the art, then, at the date of the Ritty & Birch patent: The use of keys to raise vertical rods carrying tablets was not only well known, but lies at the foundation of every cash register to which our attention has been called. It was also old to use a pivoted wing or bar to catch a projection or elbow of the vertical rod, for the purpose of holding the tablet exposed to view until another tablet was raised. . . . finally, a connecting mechanism operated by each one of the keys by means of a bar over or underneath them had been previously used for ringing the bell, opening the cash drawer, and in other machines for other purposes.
>
> What then was the contribution of this patent to the art?

The Court found the answer lay in the way the Ritty & Birch mechanism implemented these principles for more reliable operation that was less demanding of construction accuracy. Further, the court found the Boston mechanism to be not different enough to avoid infringement.[4]

This was devastation for Boston. On July 29, 1895, the lower court obediently changed its ruling and enjoined Boston from further production of its register. In October of 1896, the U.S. Marshal attached all of the assets of the Boston owners partially to cover obligations.

Boston promptly went out of business and Patterson had prevailed. The NCR/Boston fight is the earliest known competitive and legal battle in the history of the cash register business. It is one of the early examples of a company's achieving significant production but going out of business. In contrast, most of the other important competitors subsequently were acquired by NCR.

Testimony from exhibit 2198 shows that Boston patents which continued to be valid rose from the ashes several years later to bite the

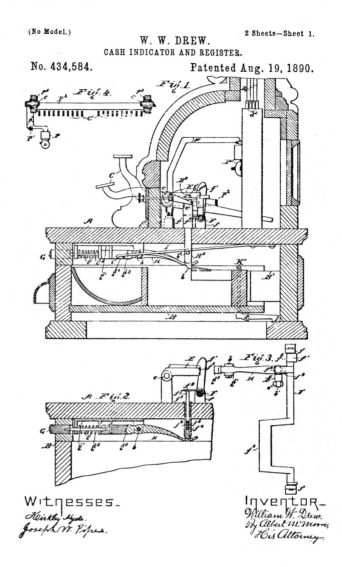

Fig. 9-9: Patent drawings for a version of the Boston. The text describes the bell-ringing operation as having the keys establish electrical contract to activate the till. This is not found on extant Bostons, or any other early register.

Globe Cash Register Company of Detroit in an infringement case.[5] Who had the teeth? NCR, naturally. Patterson purchased the Boston patents after it went out of business.

Bostons are interesting looking, well made and they are different. Their rarity and the company's early participation in the cash register field make the Boston a very desirable collectible.

[10]

Hopkins and Robinson Manufacturing Company
Louisville, Kentucky

The Hopkins and Robinson Manufacturing Company was in business at least as early as 1885. In 1886 they produced at least one type of register, a detail adder in a wood case with fancy key checks and drawer pull. Approximately ten are known to exist. The Hopkins was a nicely constructed item that must have achieved some level of distribution since it is mentioned from time to time in other cash register literature. For example, in the 1893 Standard Cash Register catalog, a letter is reproduced as a testimonial:

Gentleman:
We have been using a "Hopkins" key register for some time, but have this day discarded it for one of your Standards. We are convinced that a "black and white" record is the very best yet.

PICARD & CAPLE
Peru, Ind. 6/10/92¹

The letter refers to the lack of printer on the Hopkins as compared with the written record one gets from an autographic register.

The first known device produced by Hopkins and Robinson was a changemaker invented by Cabel B. Hopkins in 1885. Changemakers do exist and they are fine collectibles. The patent emphasizes their ability to trigger varying amounts of coins in each tube from differently denominated keys. Another important feature is the ability to disable the mechanism under lock and key. This feature was used later to link the changemaker to Hopkins' next invention, a cash register.

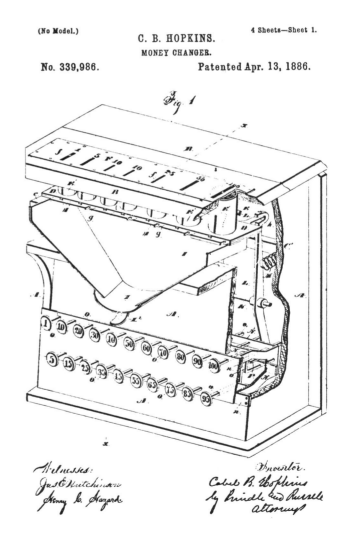

(No Model.)   C. B. HOPKINS.   4 Sheets—Sheet 1.
MONEY CHANGER.
No. 339,986.   Patented Apr. 13, 1886.

Fig. 10-1.

122

Fig. 10-2: Hopkins and Robinson changemaker, an attractive oak-encased machine.

Fig. 10-3: Hopkins and Robinson register showing unusual pull-up key operation taking advantage of thumb power.

(No Model.)

C. B. HOPKINS.
CASH INDICATOR AND REGISTER.

9 Sheets—Sheet 1

No. 384,691.   Patented June 19, 1888.

Fig. 10-4.

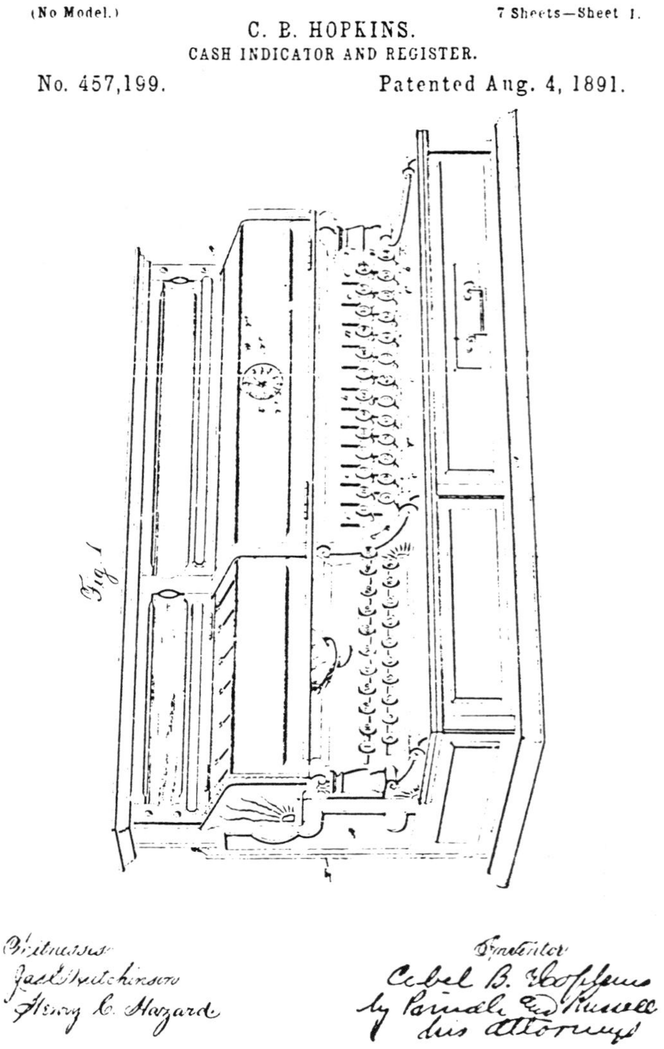

(No Model.)

C. B. HOPKINS.
CASH INDICATOR AND REGISTER.

7 Sheets—Sheet 1.

No. 457,199.   Patented Aug. 4, 1891.

Fig. 10-5.

On December 15, 1886, Hopkins filed a patent application for the detail-adder cash register. The keys worked in an inverted fashion: pulling up on them caused registration and indication.

Then, towards the end of 1888, Hopkins put the two together and filed for a patent for a combined cash register and changemaker. None of these are known to exist, but one would certainly be quite a find.

The changemaker was connected on the left side of the register in a single extended wood case with a mechanical linkage. The link caused the changemaker to lock up until the driver for the cash register bell actuated. The idea was that instead of counting out change, the clerk merely had to push the correct button on the changemaker.

This machine also had a clock that punched an annular record dial so that the clerk could leave a record of start and stop time. This machine was a time clock, cash register and changemaker all in one.

The Bensinger Cash Register Company
Chicago, Illinois

The Bensinger Cash Register Company was officially incorporated in January, 1889, as a subsidiary of the Brunswick Balke Collander Company. Brunswick was (and still is) a well-known supplier of entertainment equipment. Its Victorian back bars and high-design pool tables are valued antiques today.

Brunswick was owned by the Bensinger family. It must have seemed natural to Moses Bensinger that if they built and sold back bars, they ought to sell a cash register to go on them.

Judging from the fact that the Bensinger cash register inventor, Thomas Carney, filed for patents on the device in early 1888, it is likely that the idea was conceived in 1887 or so. Actual incorporation of a subsidiary may have been conceived when higher sales levels were contemplated.

Bensinger is mentioned in court testimony of Henry F. James, who was one of the highly visible NCR district sales managers in the 1890's. James' career in the cash register industry began at Bensinger in early 1890 as sales manager. He concentrated his efforts principally in Cincinnati and the surrounding area where National used Crane & Co. as its exclusive sales agents. James left Bensinger in the middle of 1890 to go to Crane & Co.

The earliest patent associated with Bensinger discovered so far was filed by its principal inventor, Thomas Carney, on March 5, 1888, and was granted on September 4, 1888. It was assigned to Harry G. Carney and Moses Bensinger, of Chicago, Illinois.

The "Bensinger Self Adder and Register" is an exceedingly important register since it has been discovered to be the direct ancestor of NCR's entire 35-principle and 79-principle lines of total adders. The fact that NCR used an acquired inventor to produce the technology for its most popular lines of brass registers was a surprise in this research. The discovery tended to invalidate the claim that National's own inventions department was the source of most of the early innovations in the industry. In fact, research has uncovered information that Carney may well have been the most productive inventor in early cash register history.

While National was creating the 33 principle, its first commercial total adder, Thomas Carney was creating his total adder at Bensinger. The 33 principle of NCR was embodied in the Models 30 through 38 introduced in 1890. It was a breakthrough for National because it propelled the National line into the generation of total adders that had already been created by Kruse, Boston, Bensinger and Union. But the 33 principle had design problems. It was difficult to maintain and it had a fixed, rather than modular, mechanism which was difficult to expand with features. The 33 principle died of its own obsolescence in eight short years.

Bensinger

Meanwhile, Carney seemed to want to solve every problem he ever heard of from a customer. With the Bensinger, he was concerned with the tendency in cash register drawers to work variably depending on how laden with coins the

Fig. 11-1: A photo of a fancy saloon sporting its Bensinger in what appears to be an all-metal case. This San Francisco saloon is remarkable not only for its inclusion of a Bensinger, but also a Fey Klondike counter-top color-wheel gambling machine down the counter against the wall. Courtesy Marshall Fey and the California Historical Society.

Fig. 11-2: Extant Bensinger serial #139 in "new old stock" condition. The clock face on the right side is a counter to tally the number of times the fancy oval cover is removed. Underneath is the total-adder readout. The circular tab screwed into the case on the upper right is an NCR model tag (#310) indicating this machine was once the one NCR retained for study purposes. Rick Crandall collection.

drawer became. He wanted any spring-driven drawer motion to be uniform and independent of the weight of its contents.

The resultant Bensinger register has two currency receptacles, a moveable drawer for lightweight bills, and a fixed tray protected by a flip back cover for the heavier coins.

With this arrangement, he solved a problem that it seems several companies worried about. The Chicago and the Imperial used similar strategies of uncovering the coin tray by moving the lid, rather than moving the tray. With the Chicago, once the coin tray was exposed, the drawer had to be pulled out manually after freeing a catch in order to have access to the bills. Chicago may have promoted that as a security feature.

In his 1889 patent that included the feature, Carney says:

> By this arrangement I alleviate any movement or change in the position of the coin box, and it is, therefore, not affected by any weight which it may contain, while the drawer which contains (paper) currency only is always light . . .[1]

After the Bensinger was on the market, Carney went down two parallel but separate paths of invention. One was to improve upon the Bensinger with a pull-down key approach, but redesigning the mechanism in separately removable subassemblies. This more modular design permitted more features without paying a higher price in maintainability. This effort resulted in the "35 principle," as it became known at NCR.

On the second path, he commenced work on a whole new generation of cash register technology where the register features (bell, printer, registration, etc.) were driven from a central shaft rather than from keys. The breakthrough with this design was the recognition that finger power on a press-down key register had frictional limitations depending on how strong the clerk's fingers were. With the central shaft idea, features could be added in modular fashion and driven power could be produced with a crank, taking advantage of stronger arm and wrist muscles.

Fig. 11-3: Bensinger with bill drawer extended and static coin tray uncovered. Note the use of the devil's-head pull, indicating possibly that NCR's use of the same pull was merely taking a popular design of the day.

Carney didn't stop there. His patent indicates he had electric motor operation in mind—a relatively easy task with a shaft driven register.

Neither of those inventions were completed when National came along and acquired Bensinger late in 1890. National immediately funded development of both of Carney's total-adder principles and created new NCR cases for them. With the acquisition, NCR may have had the additional motive of removing a competitor that would have been difficult to dislodge due to its stable and highly respected parent company, Brunswick.

NCR apparently wished to cover up the fact that it had acquired the Bensinger inventor. An 1892 issue of the *NCR* magazine had this to say:

> If the opposition knew what is in store for them, they would not waste any more time and money staying in the business. They are all beginning to realize that there is no hope for them. Heretofore,

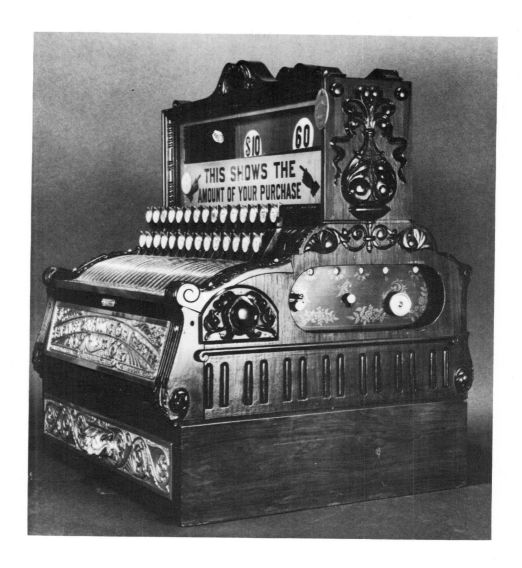

Fig. 11-4a, b: Total-adder readout under the side cover.

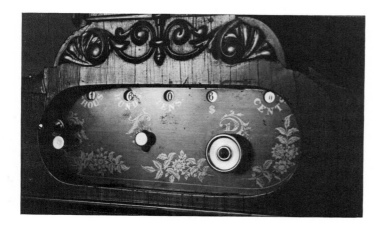

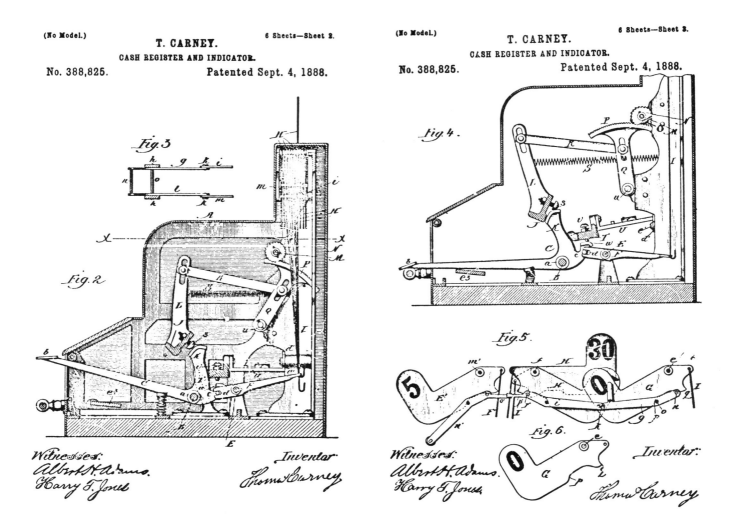

Figs. 11-5a, b, and 11-6a, b: This patent shows the actual improved machine that Carney invented and Moses Bensinger took to market. Its shape and operating principle are identical to the extant machine.

some of them have believed that Bensinger sold out to us for a large price. The idea is now exploded.

One opposition company said lately, that if we whipped the Bensinger Company, we could whip out any company that might oppose us. There was, therefore, no hope for their company because if we did not buy out Bensinger, we would not buy out any concern. We are reliably informed that Bensinger lost $67,000 in the business.[2]

Despite its claims, National proceeded to buy out not only Bensinger, but Lamson, Kruse, Osborn, Sun, Weiler, Ideal, Chicago, Union—in fact, NCR bought out every significant pre-1905 register company except Hallwood and Boston!

Testimony from the 1911 antitrust suit gives us a different perspective on Bensinger. From Henry F. James, the NCR Detroit district manager:

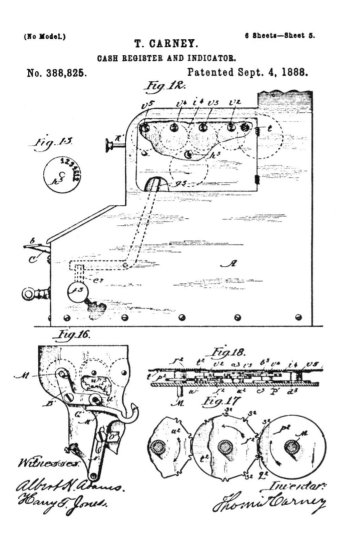

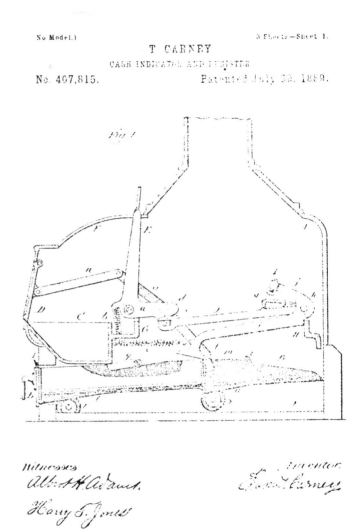

The principle total adding machine the National then had on the market was an invention of Carney, and I believe contained the improvement which Carney had invented for the Bensinger Co. . . .

. . . we had recently come into possession of a total adding machine that we secured *when we purchased the Bensinger* [italics added], a 35 principle total adding machine.[3]

And from Hugh Chalmers, NCR general manager:

The No. 35 principle machine was a total adding machine, and I think was invented or developed by Carney, at least Carney got the credit for it. He was the inventor who came to the National Company from the Bensinger Company and I think he had been a Canadian.[4]

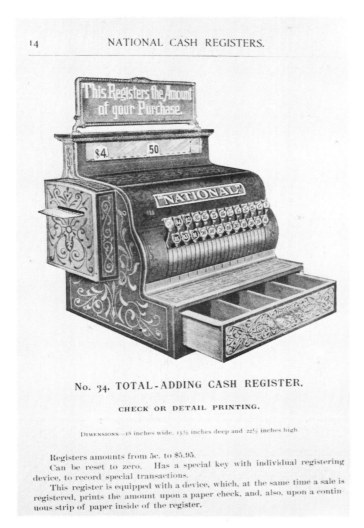

No. 34, TOTAL-ADDING CASH REGISTER,

CHECK OR DETAIL PRINTING.

DIMENSIONS—18 inches wide, 15⅜ inches deep and 22½ inches high.

Registers amounts from 5c. to $5.95.
Can be reset to zero. Has a special key with individual registering device, to record special transactions.
This register is equipped with a device, which, at the same time a sale is registered, prints the amount upon a paper check, and, also, upon a continuous strip of paper inside of the register.

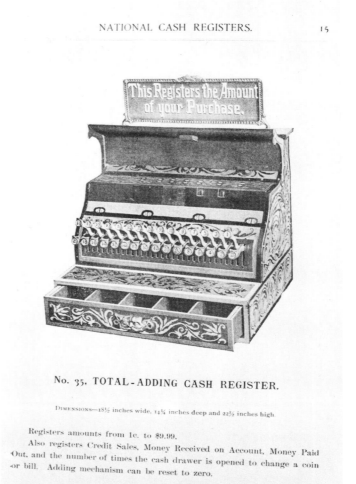

No. 35, TOTAL-ADDING CASH REGISTER.

DIMENSIONS—18½ inches wide, 14¾ inches deep and 22½ inches high.

Registers amounts from 1c. to $9.99.
Also registers Credit Sales, Money Received on Account, Money Paid Out, and the number of times the cash drawer is opened to change a coin or bill. Adding mechanism can be reset to zero.

Figs. 11-7, 8: National models in transition from the acquired Bensinger to the classic 35 principle. The shape is reminiscent of the Bensinger and key action is the same, but the fixed coin tray was eliminated and the counter readout was moved to the front.

This information on the origins of the 35 principle explains why National came out with three total-adding principles within a year where it had none previously.

Unfortunately, the Bensinger is very rare today. The one known is a high-quality, elaborate machine. It combines fancy wood cabinetry with cast bronze insets. The front casting says "Bensinger Self Adding Register" and its round-topped black-on-white indicator tabs pop up above a sign that says "This Shows the Amount of Your Purchase" that is etched in glass and backed by purple velvet. The key action is distinctive in that the operator pulls them down vertically. This action requires a less powerful finger than press-down-key registers.

[12]

The Waddel Wooden Ware Works Company
The Simplex Cash Register Company
The Sun Manufacturing Company
Greenfield, Ohio

The Waddel, Simplex and Sun companies were important early independent participants in the cash register industry. Up until recently, little history was available on these companies, yet there are enough extant registers to indicate a successful product line.

A last-minute break came when author Richard Bueschel found a stack of original files on the Waddel company. Now the history of

Fig. 12-1: Extant example of a Simplex register. Chappie collection.

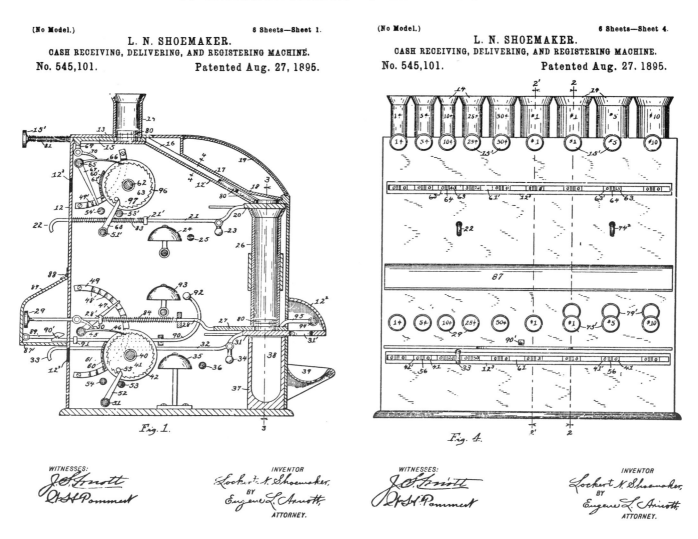

Fig. 12-2 a, b, c: L. N. Shoemaker's patent was filed March 30, 1892, and granted over three years later. It describes an unusual register where the coins are dropped in proportional-sized tubes which cause total-adding registering to occur on adder wheels. There is also provision for change-making from the bottom of the tubes and the change disbursed is also counted on adder wheels.

these companies can be told with authority.

John Mathew Waddel (1853-1922) formed the John M. Waddel Mfg. Co. in Greenfield, Ohio, in 1889. That year, the Simplex cash register was one of its first products, according to Waddel's descendent, Dean Waddel.[1]

The Waddel company letterhead asserts, "established 1889." Its articles of incorporation were dated December 18, 1891.

The Simplex was one of the first "premium" machines most usually bundled with bulk cigar purchases at wholesale. It looks like a desk register with hidden tablets for indicators.

When the clerk made a sale, he would take a shot or a clay marble and put it in the hole representing the amount desired for registration. The ball rolled down the specific chute for that amount and caused the appropriate indicator to rise.

At any time, the proprietor could unlock the lid, raise it and see at a glance how many nickel sales (balls in the nickel chute) were made, how many dime sales, etc.

The design of the machine is curiously reminiscent of the ancient Chinese abacus which also used rows of balls for each denomi-

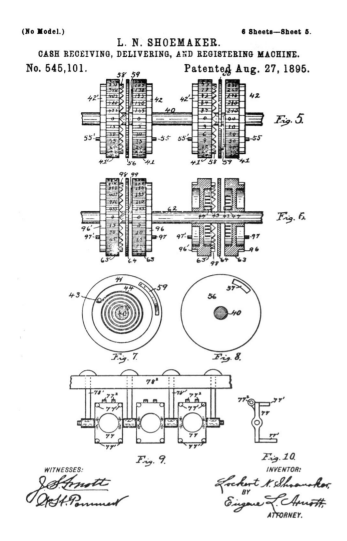

(No Model.) 6 Sheets—Sheet 5.

L. N. SHOEMAKER.
CASH RECEIVING, DELIVERING, AND REGISTERING MACHINE.
No. 545,101. Patented Aug. 27, 1895.

Fig. 5.

Fig. 6.

Fig. 7. Fig. 8.

Fig. 9. Fig. 10.

WITNESSES:

INVENTOR:
Lockert N. Shoemaker,
BY
Eugene L. Arnott,
ATTORNEY.

The Sun Manufacturing Company

On December 21, 1891, Edward L. McClain, an officer of Waddel, left and started Sun Manufacturing Company in Greenfield. There he produced the Sun cash register, a more automated device than the Simplex, that really was a cash register, keys and all. The Sun had press-down keys like a traditional register. When pressed, the key implemented its Simplex heritage by automatically dropping a marble down the chute associated with that key.

As with a conventional detail adder where a lid could always be lifted to see the status of transactions for each key, the same could be done with the Sun. Marbles did not even have to be counted because each trough had a strip of numbers alongside the string of marbles, enabling a quick reading of the appropriate number from each column. Of course, at any time the proprietor could perform the abacus-like addition to see total cash status without upsetting the day's transactions.

Fig. 12-3: Sun trademark.

nation. The abacus, however, was intended more for counting and computing than for registration, although counting-wise, the abacus could do everything the Simplex could do and more.

John Waddel renamed his company on December 22, 1900, the Waddel Wooden Ware Works Company. Simplexes were being built by a subsidiary company, The Simplex Cash Register Company. A patent (#545,101) on the register was issued on August 27, 1895, to R. N. Shoemaker.

There is evidence that the Sun was in fact inspired by the abacus. An 1896 Sun catalog claimed that although it may have seemed to the casual observer that counting marbles in each trough was a "detail adder" principle, Sun showed how it could be used as an abacus to implement a total adder!

From the catalog:

INTRODUCTION.

I N submitting our Catalogue to the public, we desire to state that we have spared neither pains nor money in producing a First-Class Cash Register, one to meet the requirements of all classes of trade.

Shrewd and careful business men recognize the advantages and necessity of Cash Registers, at the same time the keen financier considers the cost.

If the desired results can be accomplished without having to pay for expensive metal cabinet, complicated and costly mechanical construction, high priced and fancy finish, then the merchant who figures on keeping down unnecessary expenses, appreciates our efforts in producing a Cash Register, simple and effective in construction, neat and attractive in finish, that accomplishes as much as the high priced, elaborate machines, that cost several times the amount asked for the Sun No. 10.

❖ Is there a Leak in your Business? ❖

SIMPLE!		PERFECT!
THE NEW "SUN" No. 10		CASH Register
A BEAUTY!		A WINNER!

WILL STOP IT!

YOU WON'T STOP UNTIL YOU GET ONE, WHEN YOU LEARN HOW LITTLE IT COSTS.

The Sun No. 10 Register

IS MADE IN A SUBSTANTIAL, ATTRACTIVE AND WORKMAN-LIKE MANNER.

The mechanism throughout is of metal, securely mounted in a solid metal frame, which is encased in a wood cabinet of quartered oak, hard oil finish, highly polished. Natural cherry, cherry-mahogany or walnut cabinets will be furnished if desired without extra cost.

The front cover and all metal trimmings are elegant in design and nicely nickel plated.

The extreme outside measure of the Register is 19½ inches long, 17¼ inches wide, 10½ inches high in front and 19 inches high to top of glass sign.

It can be used on counter or back of it on shelf. The tablets showing the amount of the sale, plainly indicate every sale to the customer and salesman, and show from either side.

THE IMPROVED SUN NO. 10 REGISTER.

Can be Used on Counter or Shelf.

Figs. 12-4a, b, c, d, e, f, g, h, i and j: Pages from 1896 Sun sales flyer.

Showing Key Cover and Money Drawer Opened.

Can Not be Closed until Sale is Registered.

THE IMPROVED SUN NO. 10.

Combined Detail and Total Adding Cash Register and Indicator.

Showing Register Closed, after Registering Sale.

THE IMPROVED SUN NO. 10 REGISTER.

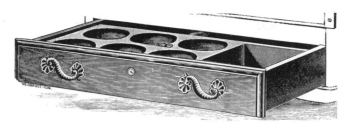

Showing Drawer Partially Open.

The Cash Drawer is conveniently arranged with six coin and three bill compartments. The coin tills are cup-shaped, to facilitate handling the money quickly.

When a sale is made, pushing the lever opens the Cash Drawer, exposes the keys and sounds the alarm gong.

This is the only way the Cash Drawer can be opened; it is automatically locked when closed.

There is an independent lock on Cash Drawer that, by locking, securely closes the Register. It can not be opened or worked until the Cash Drawer is unlocked. This is only used at times when you want to leave money in the Drawer over night, or have occasion to leave the store during business hours.

THE Keys of the Sun No. 10 Register are arranged in two rows, one above the other. The parts on which the finger is pressed are made of transparent celluloid, set in nickel plated ferrules.

There are thirty keys, one of which is tabulated "Ticket," the others being regularly arranged in denominations, as shown in cut, but can be changed to suit, from 1 cent up to $100.00.

Tablets "Paid Out," "Paid In," "Change," etc., are superfluous in any Register and are added by some manufacturers as a selling point. We have simplified matters, as the word "Ticket" covers the whole ground. In Cash Registers memorandum slips are used for such transactions. One key is sufficient for record, as the memorandum shows why Register was opened. However, if any of the above-named Tablets are wanted, we can so arrange the tabulation of Register.

The printed directions with the Sun Register give full and explicit instructions of the workings of the Register, which are very simple and easily understood.

(Reduced Size.)

CHANGE.

(Reduced Size.)

(Reduced Size.)

We furnish a supply of the above memorandum slips with each SUN No. 10 REGISTER. These slips are of different colors, "Paid Out" being blue, "Change," red, and "Received on Account," yellow. We also send blanks for taking cash footings.

To Users of No. 10 Cash Registers.

WE guarantee full protection from any infringement claimed. We hold against all comers the foundation patents on all registers we manufacture. No. 10 CASH REGISTERS are guaranteed for two years from purchase to work and accomplish all we advertise them to do.

THE SUN MANUFACTURING COMPANY,

Greenfield, Ohio, U. S. A.

THE LARGEST MANUFACTURERS IN THE WORLD OF

Cash Registers, Combined Show Case and Cash Register, Combined Show Case and Money Drawer, Combination Rolling Door Show Case with Upright Money Till and Money Drawer, also Coffee Mills and Surprise Rat Traps. Write for catalogue.

Testimonials.

We add a few testimonials from those using No. 10 Cash Registers. Its new and improved form arouses enthusiasm with every customer. We have commendations and orders that should be framed in gold. Below we submit to you the way they come, and these are customers, not agents who have sample machines on trial:

KANSAS CITY, MO., Nov. 8th, 1895.

THE SUN MANUFACTURING CO.

Gentlemen :—Please ship quick six No. 10 "Sun" Registers and follow with tracer.
Coffee and Spices. WOOLSON SPICE CO.

Western Union Telegraph Co., received at Greenfield, Ohio, Nov. 6th, 1895.

BOSTON, MASS., Nov. 6th, 1895.

To THE SUN MANUFACTURING CO.

Ship by return express four "Sun" Registers with one hundred catalogues.

WM. G. BELL & CO.

The registers were shipped promptly to Messrs. Wm. G. Bell & Co., as per telegraphic order given above. Upon their receipt they wrote us as follows:

"The register is worthy of our hearty endorsement, and that goes a good way here in New England. We know of nothing which will compare with the "Sun" No. 10 Register, when the price is taken into consideration. You certainly have made a great hit in being able to give the trade such a register at such a reasonable price. It is not only useful and attractive, but ornamental as well, and not too much so, as is the case with some of the high price registers which are placed upon the market, and of which the eye tires very soon. We expect to handle the New England trade to your entire satisfaction."

Manufacturers of Market and Grocers' Fixtures. WM. G. BELL & CO.

14

Testimonials.—Continued.

NASHVILLE, TENN., Nov. 1st, 1895.

THE SUN MANUFACTURING CO.

Dear Sirs:—We are well pleased indeed with your "Sun" No. 10 Cash Register. Please quote us your bottom price, as we will try and sell some of them. They are a good thing to have.

SMITH, HERRIN & SIMPSON,
131 to 133 N. Market St.

Manufacturers of and Dealers in Stoves, Tinware, Queensware and Glassware.

RUSSELLVILLE, KY., Nov. 7th, 1895.

THE SUN MANUFACTURING CO.

Dear Sirs:—We have been using one of your No. 10 Cash Registers for more than a year and we are sure it has systematized our business as nothing else could have done. We are well pleased with it. The new "Sun" No. 10 has several advantages over the old, and the merchants here that we interested in buying one say they are more than pleased and think the machine invaluable to any modern merchant. INMAN & CLARK.

Books, Stationery and Wall Paper.

RUSSELLVILLE, KY., Nov. 7th, 1895.

THE SUN MANUFACTURING CO.

Gentlemen:—We would not be without your No. 10 "Sun" Cash Register for three times its cost. We are surprised at its working and more than pleased with the way it systematizes our business.

Dry Goods Merchants. T. D. & W. J. EVANS.

FRANKLIN, PA., Nov. 6th, 1895.

THE SUN MANUFACTURING CO.

Gentlemen:—Ship us quick and trace ten No. 10 Registers. FREIDBURG BROS.

Wholesale Dealers in High Grade Cigars.

15

Testimonials.—Continued.

BUFFALO, N. Y., Nov. 2nd, 1895.

THE SUN MANUFACTURING CO.

Gentlemen:—We have received the improved "Sun" Register and we find by a critical examination that you have overcome all weak points on the former No. 10 "Sun" Register, and are now putting on the market the most perfect Cash Register and for the least money, not a cheap one by any means. Surely no live merchant can afford to be without one. BERNER & SCHENK,

Wholesale and Retail Hardware, Paints, Oils, Glass, &c. 515 Williams St.

PRESS OF
THE PROCTER & COLLIER CO.
315 WALNUT STREET
CINCINNATI

If so, SUN No. 10 CASH REGISTER will stop it.

This **excellent** machine is warranted **to indicate and register** odd and even **amounts**; indicate the amount of last sale **made until** next registration; show the **total amount of** sales in each denomination; **register** and indicate the amount **paid in** on account or paid out; indicate **and register** credit sales, change, tickets. **etc.**; indicate and register over $2,400 in **sales** each day.

The mechanism throughout is of metal, securely mounted in a solid metal frame, which is encased in a wood cabinet of quartered oak, hard oil finish, highly polished. Natural cherry, cherry mahogany or walnut cabinets furnished, if desired, without extra cost. The front cover and all metal trimmings are elegant in design and nicely nickel plated. The extreme outside measure of the Register is 19½ inches long, 17¼ inches wide and 10½ inches high in front and 19 inches high to top of glass sign. It can be used on the counter or back of it on a shelf. The tablets showing the amount of the sale, plainly indicate every sale to the customer and salesman, and show from either side. The cash drawer is conveniently arranged with six coin hoppers and three bill compartments. The coin tills are cup-shaped to facilitate handling the money quickly. When a sale is made, pushing the lever opens the cash drawer, exposes the keys and sounds the alarm gong. This is the only way the cash drawer can be opened; it is automatically locked when closed. Closing the drawer covers the keys, thus preventing their use except when the drawer is opened— **a feature possessed by no other Cash Register.** There is an independent lock on cash drawer that, by locking, securely closes the Register. It cannot be opened or worked until the cash drawer is unlocked, This is only used at times when you want to leave money in the drawer over night, or have occasion to leave the store during business hours. The keys of the Sun No. 10 Register are arranged in two rows, one above the other. The parts on which the finger is pressed are made of transparent celluloid, set in nickel ferrules. There are thirty keys, one of which is tabulated "Ticket," the others being regularly arranged in denominations, as shown in cut, but can be changed to suit, from 1 cent up to $100.00. The printed directions with the Sun Register give full and explicit instructions of the workings of the Register, which are very simple and easily understood.

PRICE $30.00. Send us the amount to guarantee Express charges and it will be shipped C.O.D. for the balance with privilege of examination. A special 5 per cent. discount if full amount is included with order.

Mechanically Perfect. Absolutely Correct. Largest Capacity. Beautifully Designed. Symmetrically Proportioned. Wonderfully Ingenious. It is furnished unless otherwise ordered, for **use** on the counter, and with keys tabulated from one cent to $20.00, as follows: 1c., 2c., 3c., Charge, **5c.,** 10c., 15c., 20c., 25c., 30c., 35c., 40c., 45c., 50c., 60c., 70c., 75c., 80c., 90c., No Sale, $1, $3, $4, $5, $10 and $20.

A Perfect Detail Adding Register. A Register that is Absolutely Correct.

Fig. 12-5: Ad from an 1898 Nafew (a New York distributor) catalog. Courtesy Rick Crandall.

It has all the features of a total adder . . . to illustrate, suppose the sales consist of 20 cents on the 5¢ key (i.e. four marbles), 30 cents on the 10¢ key (three marbles), 50 cents on the 50¢ key and $2.00 on the $1.00 key, you open the lid over the tray and register two balls on the 10¢ key and release the balls in the 5¢ groove [just like an abacus]. This then gives you five balls in the 10¢ groove . . .[2]

The text advocated continuing the process, emptying the five balls in the 10¢ groove and adding one to the 50¢ groove until the sum total is easily read across the grooves. The operation was extolled for its simplicity, of course, and all one has to do is witness someone who knows how to use an abacus to believe that the end-of-the-day addition with the Sun was a simpler

and more reliable task than a detail adder.

This abacus-like operation and completely different principle of registering has made the Simplex and the Sun intriguing to collectors. Of the two, the Sun is better proportioned and therefore is the more favored. Even Sun said of the Sun, "The cabinet is out in new style, better proportioned . . ."[3]

The Sun has indicators, keys, cash drawer, etc., but it is all implemented in a novel manner. Any collection designed to show the really different kinds of cash register ideas would need a Sun.

Sun registers came in two case styles. One that originally retailed for $20 was mostly wood (oak) with metal top sign and key cover. The other, which retailed for $30, has an all-metal case with a good-looking scroll design identical to the key cover on the wood version. The mechanism and indication are identical. Some Suns used a glass top sign as shown in the catalog figures.

The key cover is connected to the cash drawer so that in idle condition the keys would be covered. When a lever on the left is pushed, the cash drawer opens, the key cover opens and exposes the keys, and a bell rings. The clerk then presses the transaction value causing indication and registration. When the drawer is closed, the key cover closes over the keys. There was no key lock as part of the mechanism so the cover was Sun's way of implementing the same feature.

In its search for uniqueness at almost all cost —including market desirability—the Sun ad for the Number 10 boasts,

When a sale is made, pushing the lever opens the cash drawer, exposes the keys (a key cover slides away) and sounds the alarm gong. This is the only way the cash drawer can be opened; it is automatically locked when closed.

Closing the drawer covers the keys, thus preventing their use except when the drawer is opened—*a feature possessed by no other cash register.*[4]

Sun and Waddel parallelled each other in production of other devices, including a countertop trade stimulator called "The Bicycle." A patron would place a coin in the slot and push a lever causing the bicycle wheels to spin. When they stopped on a number, the bartender would pay winning numbers in cigars or free drinks. The Bicycle is credited as being the first commercial trade stimulator to gain national sales. First made in 1896, The Bicycle was still being made by Sun even after it moved to Columbus, Ohio, in the very early 1900's.

While NCR materials indicate that the Sun was a curiosity and not much competition, it still produced instructions for its sales representatives on how to beat it. National went so far as to sue Sun in the U.S. District Court for the Southern District of Ohio and then acquired the cash register business of the Sun Manufacturing Company in April, 1905.

There was more to Sun than cash registers and trade stimulators. Some part of Sun continued in the store showcase business independent of NCR. Eventually, the Sun Manufacturing Co. was acquired by the Columbus Show Case Co. in the middle 1920's. There are six to ten of each of the Simplex, the wood Sun and the all-metal Sun that are known to exist today, making them scarce but obtainable.

Figs. 12-6, 7: Extant Sun in all-metal case. Jimmy Filler collection.

Fig. 12-8: Close-up of Sun showing marble holders that are denominated to make the Sun a detail adder. As the balls stack up, they make columns that "point" to the cash total produced by the number of key presses for the key associated with that column. This Sun has a special key labelled "Ticket" to cumulate the number of transactions that purchased a ticket for something.

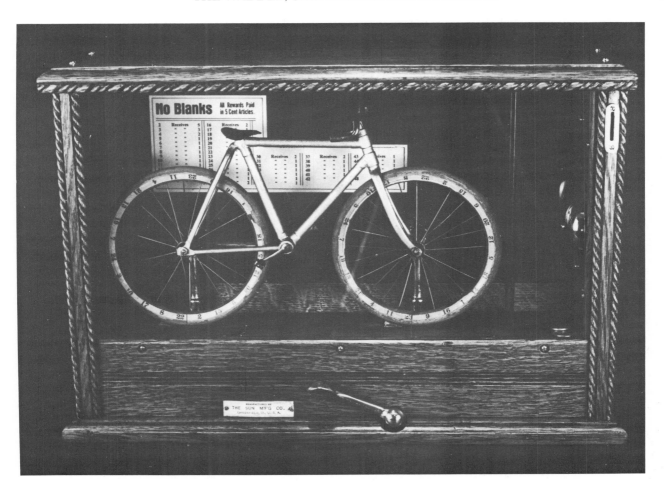

Figs. 12-9: Sun's "The Bicycle" trade stimulator. Drop a coin in the upper right hand slot, push the lever to the right and watch the tires spin. If they both land on the same number, you win some free cigars. Rick Crandall collection.

[13]

The Union Cash Register Company
Trenton, New Jersey
The Union Computing Machine Company
New York, NY

The Union Cash Register Co. was an early and resilient competitor until NCR succeeded in acquiring it. The beginnings of Union are documented in its chief inventor's own recollections, *My Half Century as an Inventor*.[1]

Fuller was connected with time-recorder work when he was asked to improve a mock-up of a cash register in 1888. Fuller writes,

I had never seen a cash register. They were not widely known, only a few merchants had them. In fact, it might be said that the cash register at that time was as rare in New England as the lion, of which there were only two or three in zoological parks.[2]

A number of Waterbury, Connecticut, men were interested in investing in Fuller's development and they took stock in the newly formed Union Cash Register Co. in 1889. After making 75 registers by hand, they moved to Trenton, New Jersey, where more funds were available. That was in 1890. In Fuller's words,

The basic difference between the Union registers and the others on the market at that time was that our machine was deliberately designed for use in general lines of retail business, whereas the others were made for and sold to saloons . . . The Union was a success from the start.

The first cash registers from our Trenton factory had a great many parts which had to be made by hand. They were just what the name implied—cash registers. That is, they made a temporary record of money paid out or taken in, but this was only until another transaction changed the figures. They had no mechanism by which a permanent record could be printed on tape. The possibility of not only printing a record for the merchant but also supplying the check receipt for the customer was one of the things I thought about constantly.

We kept steadily at the job of improving the register. I perfected and patented the printing mechanism, and also the device which would give a printed receipt to the customer. . . .

By 1907 we had thousands of cash registers in service, and by this time we had attracted the attention of the great National Cash Register Company in Dayton, Ohio.[3]

Extant models of the Union indicate that they were economically designed and effective, not cheap. Some are encased with wood sides and nickle-plated brass fronts with an unusual lever operation that make it highly collectible. Some are all brass.

Fuller recalls proudly an award his register won—the 1892 John Scott Medal of the Franklin Institute of Philadelphia.

His first registers had no tape printer, but subsequently he patented both a printer for client receipts and a tape printer to keep a record of transactions for the store owner. Fuller was constantly making improvements as exemplified by his patent #420,554, which, in the inventor's words,

> displayed to the customer's view the amount being charged for a purchase. In 1890 this was a revolutionary improvement . . . in addition to the temporary indication this made, it transfers the amount of said sale by a process of addition to a permanent totalizing register, which may be inaccessible to the salesman, and which will at all times show the sum total of sales to any person having access to the interior of the case.[4]

While many of his improvements were not exactly revolutionary, he did beat NCR to market with a total adder.

It wasn't until the next year, 1891, that National acquired Bensinger and produced its follow-on 35-principle total adder. A version of the 35 principle was packaged as a knocker to the Union.

The early 1890's were good times for Union. It moved its factory location to Trenton, New Jersey, to facilities with expanded capacity. In 1893, Union went all out to get its register into the Chicago World's Fair. The Fair was one of the biggest trade events of all time, and NCR made sure they had their registers there. Union failed in its attempt and National registers swept the fair. That was a time of targeted competition by NCR towards Union— indeed, in some cities such as St. Louis, Union was the biggest competitor.

In a March, 1893, circular, commentary ridiculing the newest Union model was as subtle as a sledgehammer:

> The National Cash Register Company Thinks One Man's Money Is As Good As Another's.
> You can buy a National cash register for just as small an amount of money as your neighbor can.[5]

On the second page of the circular appears at the top a picture of a cash register. Beneath the picture are the words,

> The New (?) Union.
> Price $125.
> Manufactured by
> The Union Cash Register Company, Trenton, New Jersey.

The cast-iron nickeled case looks different from the old wooden case, but in other respects, the new Union is substantially the same as the old.

If the Union register is worked just as you are told to work it, it may add correctly.

If everyone did just as he was told to do, a cash register would not be necessary.

A cash register on which unintentional errors are so easily made, is a dangerous register to use.

The following are the list prices of the Union registers:

Wood case	Time $100	Cash $ 85
Iron case	Time $125	Cash $110

A Few Reasons Why Progressive Business Men Have Discarded the Union Register.

> The indication of the amount purchased can be destroyed before the purchaser can possibly see the amount that was registered.
> The drawer can be opened at any time, without a record being made.
> The register can be operated at any time without closing the drawer.
> The capacity of the adding wheels of the register is only $2,000, after which it cannot be used until it is unlocked and reset.
> If the ladder [the amount lever] is used with a little too much energy it is liable to add more than the amount intended.
> A cash register composed mainly of springs and soft brass can hardly be sold upon the sole recommendation that it is cheap.

On the third page of the circular at the top appears a picture of a cash register. Under the register are the words

> No. 374. A New National.
> Price $60.
> Manufactured by
> The National Cash Register Company, Dayton, Ohio, U.S.A.
> The new No. 374 has a cast brass, nickel-plated cabinet.
> A few advantages of the No. 374 over the Union:
> More quickly operated.
> Much cheaper; much handsomer.
> Has a larger and more convenient cash drawer.

Figs. 13-1a, b: Extant Union register (serial #1329) and closeup showing the unusual lever format—actually finger holes which are denominated in standard register amounts. The operator would insert a finger in the desired cup and push down until the finger stopped at the base. Note the Patterson pull on the drawer front. Jimmy Filler collection.

Adds to $9,999.99 instead of $2,000.
It cannot be beaten. . . .

The adding mechanism is not operated by springs or constructed of soft brass.[6]

NCR brought out another knocker machine in early 1894—the Model 335 1/2. It was an out-of-sequence numbered model that was a takeoff of the popular Model 35. The 335 1/2 sold for $100 at the same time the 35 sold for $200 and the corresponding top-of-the-line Union sold for $125. It was a total adder with printer. There was also a 335 without printer. Usually, knocker registers were used to cut prices against a specific competitor without having to sacrifice profits on the normal model on sales calls where there was no competition with the targeted register.

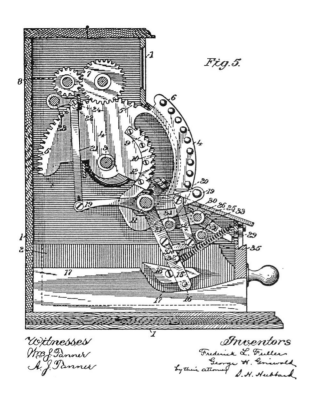

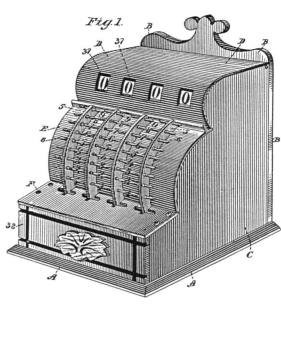

Figs. 13-2, 3, 4 and 5: Various patents granted to Fred Fuller, some as early as 1890. Nothing even close to the provocative drawing in Figure 12-4 has appeared in collector circles today.

April 3, 1894 NCR Letter to Agents
The 335 1/2 is a special register designed to compete with the Union and Hubinger-Carroll opposition. . . . These special registers should not be sold as cheap registers where a P. P.'s [Prospective Purchaser's] fixtures or stock of goods does not warrant his buying a high grade register, you are expected to sell the Nos. 5, 6, 62, etc. These are cheap machines, designed to be sold as such; and being cheap in appearance as well as price, they will not influence those who can afford better machines . . .

You should sell the special registers, which are those numbered above 300, only where absolutely necessary in order to prevent the sale of a particular opposition register with which they are designed to compete. . . . It is better to stop the sale of the opposition register and sell nothing, than to stop the sale by selling a special register. If, however, the P. P. [prospective purchaser] insists that a register without the improvements is good enough for him and has made up his mind to buy that style of register because it is cheap, and you are satisfied if you do not sell him your machine he will buy the opposition, then you should take his order for the special register, which you can do, because you have shown him it is as good as the opposition register and it is cheaper.[7]

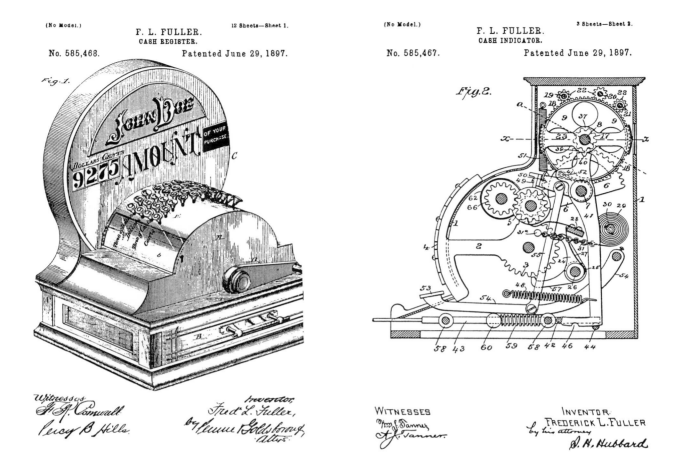

The Union Cash Register Co. went downhill after 1893 and in March of 1894 it went into receivership. The bankruptcy allowed Union to seek new financing while remaining dormant for six years. In 1900, the company re-emerged at 3 Union Square in New York City with Thomas F. Hammond as general manager and Fuller still on board. Union's general manager was a talented man having produced one of the finest of the early typewriters—the Hammond. If his influence on the Hammond was indicative of the quality of approach that he was capable of bringing to Union, then the late Union registers

benefited greatly.

The revived Union company expanded its business from 1900 to 1906, during which time the attention of National was piqued once again. National found a patent principle on which to sue Union for infringement in 1904.

National's efforts to acquire Union met with hard resistance, so an indirect method was used. Patterson set up a secret fund and placed it at the disposal of Edgar Park. Under the cover of an independent investor with deep pockets, Park succeeded in buying the Union with cash and the promise to fund an expansion program against National. The purchase was consummated on November 1, 1906, at which time the name was changed to the Union Computing Machine Co. Subsequently, the Union was operated without knowledge of the NCR ownership until July of the following year when it was shut down.

The following examples from a series of letters describe the conditions at the time and the final demise of Union:

[Letterhead of the Union Computing Machine Company, Union Cash Registers, 3 Union Square, West, New York, N.Y., U.S.A.]

January 18, 1907.
Edgar Park, President
Thomas F. Hammond, Treasurer and
General Manager
Frederick L. Fuller, Secretary.
[To]Messrs. Cowen-Heineberg Co.,
San Francisco Cal.
[A Union sales agent]

Dear Sirs:
Since we determined about a year ago, that it would be desirable sooner or later, to provide our agents and selling connections with a check printing device for our machines, we have, as has been stated in our correspondence with you from time to time forced the development of such a device in our factory by every means possible. The announcement made to our various connections about six months ago, to the effect that our check printer was about ready, was made in absolute confidence that within sixty days of that time we could produce check printing machines in considerable quantities, and resulted in the receipt by us of orders for a very large number of these machines, these orders not being open on our books.

After a very large expenditure and the exercise of a great deal of patience on the part of our selling connections as well as ourselves, we think it only fair at this date to announce to you that we have come to the conclusion that our check printing device is not sufficiently well developed to warrant our putting it out as a commercial article until it has had considerable further test and has been slightly altered mechanically.

This statement is, from our standpoint, a most important one, and is made to you in the most confidential nature, only because we believe it to be our duty to you to keep you fully apprised of the conditions here, and because we are convinced that it would be unwise to hasten the sale of the check printer at a sacrifice which would be the inevitable result if it did not prove absolutely satisfactory when undergoing the severe test of general usage.

We will continue to manufacture the total adding machine and the strip printing machine, with improvements which insure its being even more satisfactory than in the past, and we believe that the large field of opportunity which these models enjoy will enable our agents to continue to build up an increasingly profitable trade with these models alone.

As to the delivery of the check printer, it is only fair to say that it may be from four to eight months from January 1st before we are ready to fill the orders which we have on our books. . . .

In the decision above given to you, we have been influenced by our former experience of the strip printer and the annoyance that our customers and ourselves were put to because of the weakness that developed when we thought the machine was practically perfect. . . .

You will note the change in the name of our company, and we beg to advise you that the company is now in the hands of a new group which represents a large amount of capital, and whose policy it will be to perfect the machine absolutely before offering it for sale, and also that this new group feels that the old company made a mistake in offering the check printer prematurely.

We have eliminated all of the weak points of the total adder and the strip printer, especially the difficulty that caused the balling up, the difficulty with the 79 coil spring, and the brass collars B69 and B74 are now replaced with strong collars made of steel. All the former parts which were liable to break are now made of steel, so that we have today a combined total adder and strip printer that we can recommend and that has been sold to many of our dealers near home who have expressed satisfaction with the improvement that we have made in these strip printers, so that you can, with confidence, send us your orders for total adders and strip printers, and be sure that you will receive machines that you and your customers will be pleased with, on reasonably early deliveries.

We congratulate ourselves upon having such worthy representatives in your territory, and hope that you can adjust your business arrangements so that you can continue to represent us as we can, without doubt, complete and perfect the check printer within a reasonable length of time.

May we expect your orders for strip printers and total adders such as our 643 and 649 and our 603 and 609?

Thanking you for your previous orders, and hoping that we can soon establish a mutually pleasant and profitable business between us, we remain,

Yours truly,
Union Cash Register Company
(Signed) Thomas F. Hammond,
G.M.[8]

[Letterhead of the Weiler Cash Register Company.]
Detroit, Mich.,
February 18, 1907.
[To]Union Cash Register Co.,
San Francisco, Cal.

Gentlemen:
As per our letter agreement with your Mr. Blessing, I hereby notify you that the Weiler Cash Register Co. has sold out to the National Cash Register Co. of Dayton, Ohio.

Mr. Blessing has an agreement from us in letter form, so, if you are able to reach him, I would advise that you write him this information, inasmuch as Mr. Blessing has entered into a contract with the Weiler Cash Register Co., and this information will be of considerable interest to him.

Yours truly,
The Weiler Cash Register Co.,
G. A. Wineman,
Gen. Mgr.[9]

March 1, 1907.
Weiler Cash Register Co.,
Champlain and Beaubein Sts.,
Detroit, Michigan

Gentlemen:
Your valued favor of the 18th of February advising us of the sale of your factory to the National Cash Register Co. was a great surprise to us, coming as it did almost immediately after the writer's visit to your factory. [this is three months after Union had unknowingly also sold out to NCR!] We thank you for your prompt notification and shall no doubt be glad to avail ourselves of the privilege of placing an order with you for the number of registers provided for in our agreement.

However, there are a few points which are not clear to us and we would appreciate it if you will give us what information you can, that is, if the information we desire, does not conflict in any way with your policy or arrangements.

Is it the intention to continue the manufacture of registers for some time or for any stated time, and what would you consider a reasonable time for us to take both our order already placed with you for this year and the order we have the privilege of placing at our option, also can we depend on the quality of the registers you would ship us. Also, will you provide us with sufficient parts for repair purposes for whatever number of registers we purchase.

We are somewhat disappointed in receiving no notice of the shipment of the parts promised the writer. Have you made shipment of these?

Thanking you in advance for this information, we beg to remain,

Very truly yours,
Union Cash Register Company
Secretary[10]

Weiler had also sold out to Park and Park "sold" Weiler to NCR before "reselling" Union to NCR.

March 1, 1907.
[To]Union Cash Register Company,
No. 1 Union Square, West,
New York, N.Y.

Gentlemen:
We beg to acknowledge receipt of your favor of the 25th of February addressed to Cowen-Heineberg Co., and beg to advise that we have already received the name plates.

We require another name plate for one of the new models just sold and attach below the details of same.

Most of the last shipment received from you are already in use and we are watching them with considerable interest and hope that the bubble will not break. We understand that Mr. Park has disposed of the Weiler factory to the N.C.R. Co. It just happens that we have an option of placing an order large enough for our needs for some time to come with the Weiler factory, but are awaiting further developments with much interest.

Any light you can give us on the subject will be greatly appreciated by the writer as a favor from Mr. Hammond.

Thanking you for your favors, we beg to remain,

Very truly yours,
Union Cash Register Company
Secy.[11]

[Letterhead of the Union Cash Register Company, Manufacturers of Union Cash Registers, Union Square, West, New York, NY, U.S.A.]

March 7, 1907.

Messrs.
Union Cash Register Co.,
San Francisco, Cal.

Dear Sirs:

We are in receipt of yours of March 1st, acknowledging the receipt of ours of the 25th of Feb. Glad to know that you received the name plates and note your order for an additional one for Handelmans Cafe.

We are very much pleased to know that the last shipment received by you are already in use and that you are watching them with considerable interest.

We would appreciate very much when you refer to shipments if you would mention the date of the shipment that you refer to as we are literally in the dark as to just which shipment you refer.

We note your reference to the disposal of the Weiler factory by our president to the N.C.R. Co. and would say that your understanding of the matter is correct, and that in disposing of this plant he did so only with a specified agreement that all suits against the Union Computing Machine Co. or its successors, the Union Cash Register Co. should be withdrawn, so that you will see at once that it is of very decided advantage to the U.C.R. Co.

We also note what you say in reference to having an option on placing a large order which will supply your needs for some time to come.

Any further information that we can give you we shall be very glad to do so.

Very truly,
Union Cash Register Company
Thomas F. Hammond

May 3, 1907.

[To]Union Cash Register Company,
Trenton, New Jersey.

Gentlemen:

Referring to your favor of the 18th of April, which was received during the writer's absence, we note the receipt by you of our order for two Model 643 and we wish specially to ask that you give us as prompt delivery as possible on these as we wish them for replacement purposes. We note what you state regarding the guarantee and that you cannot agree to pay freight one way on any more defective registers, and shall govern ourselves accordingly. Kindly advise us as to how many of these registers have arrived at Trenton up to this writing and when we can expect the return of these to us. The indifference with which our complaints of April 9th seem to have been taken, coupled with persistent reports both here and in Los Angeles, that the Union factory is about to sell out have led to conclusions that possibly a change is about to happen. We will appreciate it if you can keep us informed on these different matters, so that we can know how to provide for emergencies.

Very truly,
Union Cash Register Company
Secty.[12]

[Letterhead of the Union Cash Register Company, New York, NY, U.S.A.]

Trenton, New Jersey,
May 13, 1907.

[To]Messrs.
Union Cash Register Company,
529 Market Street,
San Francisco, Cal.
[A Union sales office]

Dear Sirs:

We have your letter of May 3rd, and will ship the two Model 643, not later than May 18th. We can promise delivery on all future orders within ten days from receipt of the same. We wish you would kindly anticipate your orders somewhat, as we expect within the next month or five weeks to raise the price on all the machines which we are now making. In reference to the machines that have been returned to Trenton: up to the present writing we have received 9, 4 of which we will return to you on May 14. The balance will go forward within a few days. We also have bills of lading for four more, which have not yet been received at Trenton, but as Mr. Hammond, our former general manager, has agreed to accept only 12 of these machines, we will be obliged to charge on your next bill, freight from San Francisco to Trenton, on the last machine shipped.

In reference to the reports which you have heard in San Francisco and Los Angeles, that the Union factory is about to sell out, in answer would state that these reports are absolutely without foundation and are circulated by people who have an idea that they will injure our business somewhat, by circulating these reports.

Yours very truly,
Union Cash Register Company
G. A. Wineman
Assistant G. M.

Gustave Wineman was brought in by Park to replace Hammond. Wineman later testified that at this point he still didn't know that Park *was* NCR.

[Letterhead of Union Cash Register Company. Edgar Park, President, New York, NY., U.S.A.]
Trenton, New Jersey,
July 27, 1907.
Personal.
[To]Mr. Charles Blessing, Sec'y.
Union Cash Register Company,
529 Market Street,
San Francisco, Cal.

Dear Sir:
Owing to the lack of sufficient orders, the Union Cash Register Co. has discontinued the manufacture of Union cash registers for the American market. In other words, the Union Cash Register Company has gone out of business.

Yours very truly,
Union Cash Register Company
G. A. Wineman
Assistant G. M.[13]

[14]

The Chicago Cash Register Company (also The Navy Cash Register Company)
Chicago, Illinois

The Chicago Cash Register Company was an early entrant in the business with a line of registers based on patents of Luke Cooney, Jr. of Kalamazoo, Michigan. The patents give an idea that probable formation date was in the 1890-93 period. Chicago's president was Robert L. Henry. One Chicago catalog boasted a production capacity of 300 registers per day, but it is doubtful real production reached levels that high.

Sometime between 1894 and 1899, Chicago was somehow acquired by or transformed into The Navy Cash Register Company. On January 26, 1900, NCR sued Navy for injunctive relief in the U. S. Circuit Court, Northern District of Illinois, Northern Division. The really odd fact about this suit was that National was suing Navy four days before the expiration of the Ritty & Birch patents against which infringement was being claimed!

One of the unusual features of the Chicago is the way the "Union" key could be pressed and then a succession of value keys could be pressed to ring up a high-value transaction. The court opinion acknowledges the novelty of that feature:

Upon the question of infringement, it is true that defendant's [Navy] device is a decided advance upon that covered by complainant's [National's] patent. It enables the operator, by a system of segregated working bars, to combine figures with ease—something that complainant's device accomplishes with considerable awkwardness and difficulty; . . .[1]

The injunction did not issue and it is not known what the next legal steps were nor whether it mattered given the peculiar timing of the circumstances.

Known Navys are identical to the Chicago except for the drawer pull which is surrounded by a plaque with "The Navy" cast in it.

The Company was eventually acquired by National on October 2, 1905.

Luke Cooney, Jr., received three patents for his novel ideas in cash register design and anyone who has seen a Chicago will notice its differences. Among his many patent claims were various designs which achieved manufacturing reliability and simplicity. In patent #555,302, issued on February 25, 1896, claims include:

1. Dispensing with springs wherever possible, using gravity instead.
2. Detention of any key until pushed to the limit, avoiding registration tricks and errors that failed some other register makes.
3. Operation of only one key at a time (although in actual implementation this is only true within a single-key section governed by one of the total adders).
4. Locking of all keys when the money drawer is open, thereby forcing the user to close the drawer after each transaction (although in actual implementation this feature was not used).[2]

In another of his patents, we find the objective of the improvements were

To simplify the mechanism and working parts of a

Fig. 14-1: Bar scene with a Chicago register in the background showing a customized top sign that was undoubtedly the name of the establishment, "Smith & Allen." Courtesy Henry Bartsch.

cash register so that it is not necessary to use micrometers or delicate and costly machinery to construct a cash register, for when so constructed, hard and continued usage will soon make an imperfect machine and with some of the highest priced and so-called best machines a careless or scheming operator will in short time destroy the accuracy.[3]

Luke Cooney, Jr., further claimed,

In cash register phraseology the term "pumping" is often used, that is if a register can be pumped, it is imperfect as it affects the registration. The usual way of pumping is to work a key part way up and down between the upper and lower positions so as to move the register mechanism and, thereby, cause imperfect registration.

In order to have in view more than one indicator tablet at the same time, various means have been devised to do this, but they are correct in theory only. One of the most recent methods is what is known as a key coupler which allows the operator to depress a key a limited distance and then another key in like manner and then by depression of the third key to its full stroke it brings down the other two partly depressed keys to their full

Fig. 14-2, 3, and 4.

strokes respectively, but if the operator should happen to depress the first or second key further than the limit, it will be readily seen that the third key would have no effect in depressing them farther and therefore the desired work not achieved.

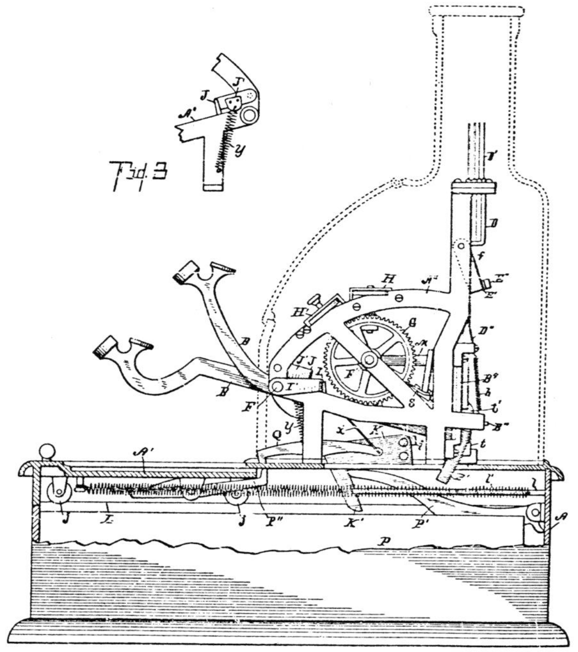

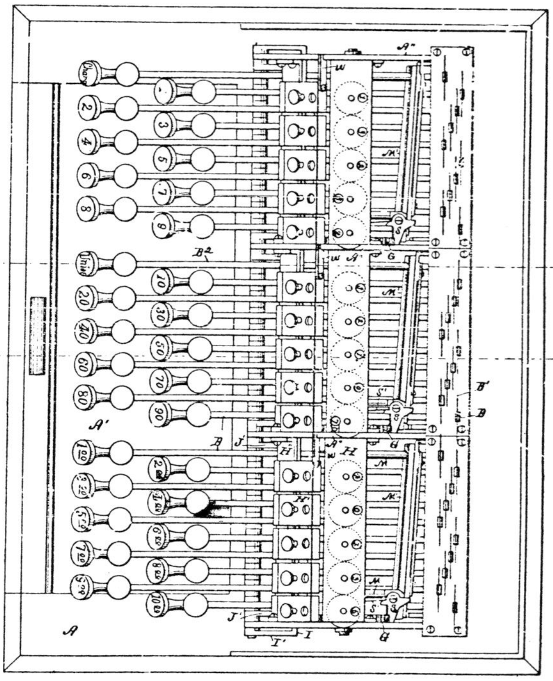

In my new method I use the Union key . . . the first of its kind as a connecting mechanism for more than one indicator tablets with absolute positiveness.[4]

In appearance, the Chicago is also unique, although some appearance items were not claimed in the patents, possibly indicating that other patents had established similar claims.

The Chicago cash drawer is a surprise—when a key is pressed, instead of seeing the cash drawer pop out the front, the top cover of the drawer pops back into the machine thereby exposing the front coin-trays portion. If access to the bills trays (located behind the coin trays) is desired, the operator pushes a detent button under the front handle and pulls the drawer out. Cooney undoubtedly solved the same problem that Carney of Bensinger was worried about. The variability of weight of coins in a moveable drawer causes it to pop out a variable distance. By making the moveable drawer hold bills only, the problem was avoided.

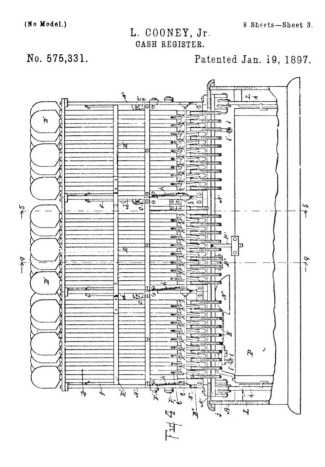

(No Model.)

L. COONEY, Jr.
CASH REGISTER.

8 Sheets—Sheet 3.

No. 575,331.

Patented Jan. 19, 1897.

Witnesses:
H. S. Wood
V. E. Chappell

Inventor.
Luke Cooney Jr.
By Fred L. Chappell
Att'y.

The Chicago has two pods per key, one offset 90 degrees from the other. One circular pod holds the value of the key (1¢, 10¢, etc.) and the other pod is the surface for pushing to activate the key. This eliminated wear on the numbers allowing them to retain their clarity.

The gleaming nickel-plated cast-metal cases on some Chicago registers are the most deeply and elaborately carved metal cases made by any manufacturer. These so-called "High Art" machines were the fanciest registers on the market. The flowing carvings were even carried to portions of the machine under cover—namely the normally locked area of the adders

that was usually viewed only by the proprietor. There were other designs that were very attractive, but not quite as elaborate. Some Chicagos came in a scroll metal cabinet and others were offered in mahogany or oak wood. One case variant is a combination of nickelled-metal framing with oak or mahogany inset panels.

Most models were offered with or without a cash drawer. Chicago advertised that if their register was purchased without a cash drawer, it could be used with any existing cash drawer already in the store, thereby saving $10 to $15 in price. The idea of using a register to trigger a "foreign" drawer was another difference in Chicago's marketing approach.

Chicago felt unhampered by the use of the label "Change" for what NCR called the "No Sale" key.

Chicago had a high-class product and they were proud of it. Their catalog offer stated,

We will give $1,000 in gold to any person or persons who will show us a cash register that was ever manufactured and sold by any other cash register company in the world that is, in appearance, principle, capacity or absolute correctness of the work performed, like our Register No. 49 . . .[5]

Even the Chicago Cash Register Company had to take an oblique shot at NCR's methods with a specific mention in their catalog of

Our Methods
We sell all of our High-Grade Total Adding Cash Registers on their merits at honest prices, and not on the demerits of other registers or other register companies.[6]

The Chicago boasted over 50 models, all total adders with differences being largely the capacity and number of trays.

Model 3: 5¢ to 50¢, 12 keys; a small register for cigar stores and soda fountains.
Model 5: 5¢ to $5.00, 15 keys; a register for hotels, cafes and buffets.
Model 7: 1¢ to $1.00, 17 keys; includes optional color system, for small general retail stores, cigar and drug stores.
Model 9: 1¢ to $5.00, 19 keys; for drug and

Fig. 14-5, 6, and 7: Extant Chicago Model 17 with sectioned
keyboard and two separate total adders (a sophisticated
feature for the middle 1890's). Rick Crandall collection.

Fig. 14-8, 9: Extant Chicago Model 12 front and rear views. Robert Gilson collection.

Fig. 14-10: Extant Chicago Model 3 with single counter.

grocery stores, small dry goods
stores or any general store.

Model 12: 1¢ to $1.00, 21 keys; for grocery stores,
drug stores, paper and cigar stores,
confectionary stores, etc.

Model 17: 5¢ to $1.00, 22 keys; for cigar stores,
small saloons, restaurants.

Model 31: 1¢ to $5.00, 25 keys; "with all the latest
and best improvements, the best
machine on the market for grocers,
and druggists and any general store
using pennies."
Finished in high-art metal cabinet.

Model 49: 5¢ to $1,000, 40 keys; for banks and
wholesale houses.[7]

The Chicago holds a special place in the hearts
of the collecting community. It combines
unusual mechanical features, quality of operation, rarity and great beauty in a cash register.

In sophistication of features, the Chicago was
comparable to other press-down key machines
of the period, although it was among the highest
quality and was certainly attractively priced in
the $50 to $115 range. Three existing examples
of the Model 31 also sport a sectional total-
adder mechanism mentioned in the catalog,
which may be what is referred to as "latest
improvements." The term "sectional total adder"
refers to the existence of an adder for each of
two sections of the keyboard allowing a color
system on the keys to separate transactions
amongst two departments or clerks.

Endnotes

Chapter 2

[1]U. S. Patent #221360 issued to James Ritty and John Ritty, March 26, 1879.
[2]*Scientific American*, February 16, 1878, p. 95.
[3]U. S. Patent #188,310 issued to H. S. Smith and John Moss on March 13, 1877, and assigned to Erastus Wiman.
[4]*Scientific American*, February 16, 1878, p. 95.

Chapter 3

[1]U. S. Patent #271,363 issued to James Ritty and John Birch, January 30, 1883, and assigned to Jacob H. Eckert.
[2]National Cash Register Company v. Boston Cash Indicator and Recorder Company, et al, U. S. Circuit Court, District of Massachusetts, March 23, 1891, No. 2405.
[3]National Cash Register Company v. Boston Cash Indicator and Recorder Company.

Chapter 4

[1]Samuel Crowther, *John H. Patterson, Pioneer in Industrial Welfare* (New York: Doubleday Page & Co., 1923), pp. 58-59.
[2]U. S. Patent #318,506 issued to James Ritty, May 26, 1885, and assigned to the National Manufacturing Company.
[3]John Patterson's Story, in an undated NCR flyer from the early 1900's.
[4]"What Is A Cash Register," *American Storekeeper*, August, 1886.

Chapter 5

[1]Frederick L. Fuller, *My Half Century As An Inventor* (New York: n.p., 1938), p. 27.
[2]Fuller, *My Half Century*, p. 37.
[3]Isaac F. Marcossen, *Wherever Men Trade: The Romance of the Cash Register* (New York: Dodd, Mead & Company, 1947), p. 93.
[4]Fuller, *My Half Century*, preface.
[5]Marcossen, *Wherever Men Trade*, p. 96.
[6]Marcossen, *Wherever Men Trade*, p. 98.
[7]Marcossen, *Wherever Men Trade*, pp. 98-100.
[8]U. S. v. NCR, p. 480.
[9]Hallwood Guarantee, ca. 1900.
[10]Hallwood Guarantee, ca. 1900.
[11]U. S. v. NCR, p. 482.
[12]U. S. v. NCR.
[13]According to Marcossen, *Wherever Men Trade*, p. 105.
[14]According to Marcossen, *Wherever Men Trade*, p. 106.
[15]U. S. v. NCR, pp. 1-17.
[16]*N.C.R.*, March 15, 1892, p. 517.
[17]*N.C.R.*, May 1, 1892, p. 556, as quoted in U. S. v. NCR, p. 989.
[18]*N.C.R.*, May 1, 1892, p. 519, 554-555, as quoted in U. S. v. NCR, p. 989.
[19]U. S. v. NCR, p. 295.
[20]U. S. v. NCR, p. 141.
[21]Undated NCR flyer, ca. 1902.
[22]U. S. v. NCR, p. 498.
[23]U. S. v. NCR, p. 489.
[24]As reported in "Competition in the Cash Register Business," *N.C.R.*, June 15, 1895, p. 414.
[25]"Competition in the Cash Register Business," p. 414.
[26]Testimony of Hugh Chalmers, U. S. v. NCR, p. 487.

[27]U. S. v. NCR, p. 1143.
[28]U. S. v. NCR.
[29]U. S. v. NCR, pp. 1061, 1067.
[30]"History of Computing," *Computerworld*, November 3, 1986, p. 183.
[31]U. S. v. NCR, pp. 262-263.
[32]U. S. v. NCR, pp. 276-279.
[33]U. S. v. NCR, pp. 330-339.
[34]U. S. v. NCR, pp. 196-199.
[35]As quoted in U. S. v. NCR, p. 1063.
[36]Originally appeared in *N.C.R.*, July 15, 1892, p. 625; as quoted in U. S. v. NCR, p. 998.

Chapter 6

[1]Marcossen, *Wherever Men Trade*, p. 50.
[2]Marcossen, *Wherever Men Trade*, p. 30.
[3]Stanley C. Allyn, *My First 50 Years in Dayton* (Dayton, Ohio: Winters National Bank and Trust Co., 1963), p. 8.
[4]Allyn, *My First 50 Years*, p. 14.
[5]Allyn, *My First 50 Years*, p. 15.
[6]Allyn, *My First 50 Years*, p. 12.
[7]U. S. v. NCR, pp. 455, 466-467.
[8]U. S. v. NCR, p. 467.
[9]U. S. v. NCR, pp. 424-425.
[10]U. S. v. NCR, pp. 447-448.
[11]Crowther, *John H. Patterson*, pp. 237-240.

Chapter 7

[1]Crowther, *John H. Patterson*, p. 83.

Chapter 8

[1]NCR flyer, 1893, Sam Robins Collection.

Chapter 9

[1]From affidavit of John H. Patterson filed May 16, 1888, in support of National Cash Register Company vs. Boston Cash Indicator and Recorder Co. in the U. S. Circuit Court, District of Massachusetts, No. 2619.
[2]*N.C.R.*, October 1, 1894.
[3]NCR v. The Boston Cash Indicator and Recorder Company, U. S. Supreme Court, October Term, 1894, cause #155.
[4]NCR v. Boston, as quoted in U.S. v. NCR, p. 1346.
[5]U. S. v. NCR, p. 1572.

Chapter 10

[1]Catalogue in the Rick Crandall Collection.

Chapter 11

[1]Patent #407,815, issued to Thomas Carney on July 30, 1889.
[2]John H. Patterson, *N.C.R.*, May 1, 1892, p. 561-562.
[3]U. S. v. NCR, p. 98.
[4]U. S. v. NCR, p. 494

Chapter 12

[1]Letter from Dean Waddel to Richard Bueschel, October 28, 1975.
[2]Sun catalog, Rick Crandall Collection.
[3]Sun catalog, Rick Crandall Collection.
[4]Samuel Nafew & Company, New York, catalog ca. 1898, Rick Crandall Collection.

Chapter 13

[1]Fuller, *My Half Century*.
[2]Fuller, *My Half Century*, p. 20.
[3]Fuller, *My Half Century*, p. 27.
[4]U. S. Patent #420,554 issued to Frederick Fuller.
[5]U. S. v. NCR, p. 1078.
[6]U. S. v. NCR, p. 1078.
[7]U. S. v. NCR, pp. 1069-1071.
[8]U. S. v. NCR, pp. 1044-1046.
[9]U. S. v. NCR, p. 1046.
[10]U. S. v. NCR, p. 1047; the secretary who sent the letter was Charles Blessing in the San Francisco sales office.
[11]U. S. v. NCR, p. 1047; the secretary who sent the letter is Charles Blessing in the San Francisco sales office.
[12]The secretary who sent the letter is Charles Blessing in the San Francisco sales office.
[13]U. S. v. NCR, pp. 1044-1046, 1050.

Chapter 14

[1]NCR vs. Navy Cash Register Co., et al., Circuit Court, Northern District Illinois, Northern Division, Jan 26, 1900, as recorded in U. S. v. NCR, p. 1477.

[2]U. S. Patent #555,302 issued to Luke Cooney, February 25, 1896.

[3]U. S. Patent #575,331 issued to Luke Cooney.

[4]U. S. Patent #575,331 issued to Luke Cooney.

[5]Chicago catalog, Sam Robins Collection.

[6]Chicago catalog, Sam Robins Collection.

[7]Chicago catalog, Sam Robins Collection.

Glossary of Terms

Adding Wheels   Rotating wheels used in the various kinds of display counters found in cash registers. Usually numerals from 0 to 9 were stamped around the edge (e.g. where the tread is on a tire) in a full circle. Some have paper with imprinted numerals glued around the perimeter. Adding wheels were used to count key presses, cash values, numbers of customers, sales per clerk, credit transactions, etc. They are the basic accounting device of the cash register.

Audit Trail   Usually a printed record of each transaction in order of occurrence; with regard to cash registers an audit trail was a strip of paper that rolled up into the register and on which were printed the cash values of every key press in sequence. These are usually called detail strips. Audit trails were used to track back in order to verify transactions or to find errors.

Autographic   In broad terms, autographic means a device that allowed the clerk to hand write on a strip of paper that was retained on a roll in the register. In some cases, a multi-part receipt was used where the register kept a continuous copy and another copy was given to the customer.

There are registers that are solely autographic, operating entirely on the principle that a handwritten receipt for the customer was sufficient. A duplicate copy stored under lock and key allowed the proprietor to sum the cash totals manually at the end of the day.

Autographic features on adding cash registers allowed the clerk to annotate a printed receipt and/or to make notes about such things as stock reordering during the course of a day. On an NCR 500-Class machine, the word "autographic" was used two ways: 1) a standard autographic attachment called a "Things Wanted" device, manually advanced and used as a scratch pad. 2) the optional autographic "G" printer that could be ordered for narrower printer paper. These Autographic printers had their paper advanced by the register in synchronization with the detail strip so that transactions could be annotated individually. Autographic attachments are usually desirable options from a collector's point of view.

Bill Weights   Metal weights about the size of a dollar bill and 1/4" thick; usually nickel plated with a fancy design. Bill weights were used in each bill compartment of the cash drawer to keep crumpled bills flat and in order. A later type of bill weight consisted of spring wires with a weight to hold down bills.

Brass   A mixture or alloy of copper plus small amounts of tin, nickel and zinc. The word "brass" is usually used to refer to yellow brass, an alloy usually containing 71% copper resulting in a yellow color.

Bronze   A copper alloy. Usually, the word "bronze" refers to an alloy that is slightly more reddish in color than yellow brass. The more reddish color comes from a higher proportion (usually 85%) of copper.

Candy Store Registers   A term usually used to refer to almost any press-down key small cash register (10 to 15 keys in two rows). In fact, candy store registers were more specifically the small machines that had key arrangements beginning at one cent (vs. saloon registers on which key values began at five cents).

Charge   A key set up to annotate the detail strip printer paper with a symbol to indicate a credit transaction. The "Charge" key could also be set up so that the credit amount did not add into the total adder, thereby maintaining consistency with the amount in the cash drawer.

Check   In cash register terminology, "check" means a receipt cut from the register's check printer on which the sales price is printed. Checks could be embellished with sayings, logos or special promotional messages using custom-made electrotypes.

Check Box   A high-design, secured box with a slot on top into which checks could be deposited. Check boxes were used in situations where checks were tickets purchased at one place and turned in at another.

Class   A term introduced by NCR in 1908 to differentiate register groupings, each based on a different technical operating principle. For example, the 200 Class were the detail adders.

Clock   see Time Recorder.

Coin Compartment   NCR provided a metal-covered coin compartment as an option in one of the bins of the cash drawer. It had a slot so that money could be dropped into it. Some merchants would secure gold coins in this compartment. NCR recommended that it be used like a bank to put away a small amount each day to make the register payments.

Color System   A term used to describe the use of different colors for groupings of key checks that were to be associated with different departments.

Counter   A mechanical adder consisting of interconnected wheels that added and displayed correct multi-digit totals. The wheels had numbers stamped or printed on the surfaces.

Counter Cabinet   A base cabinet used on some NCR registers in place of a single cash drawer. Counter cabinets had up to five drawers in a single tier or up to eight drawers in a double tier; drawer selection and opening was controlled from the register.

Crank   Refers to both removeable cranks used to reset register counters to zero or to the crank on crank-powered registers such as NCR's 79 principle. NCR also called cranks used for powering registers "handles." Cranks were useful when extra power was needed for added register functions since they operated from hand, wrist and arm power, not just finger power.

Credit   A privilege extended to preferred customers where they could charge purchases in a way similar to credit card use today. Special keys were usually employed to implement charge accounts; see "Charge" and "Received on Account" keys.

Credit System   Usually this term was used to describe a credit slip storage cabinet that was specially designed for organized storage and retrieval of paper slips. McCaskey was a popular manufacturer of a credit system and NCR made a credit storage cabinet.

Customer Counter   A counter appearing on some registers that counted and displayed the number of registrations made since the last key press. The assumption made was that there was only one registration for each customer, necessitating multiple item purchases being added by hand.

Decimal Adder   An adder that used adder wheels with the numerals 0 to 9 on them. The wheels were interlinked so that when a wheel of lower value rotated a complete revolution, as it approached its zero digit, it caused the adder wheel of the next highest value (i.e. next to the left) to increase by one. This implemented the arithmetic carrying principle allowing, for example, 09 to turn into 10. There were non-decimal adders, for example, such as those in use on English machines that handled shillings and pence.

Deep Drawer   A common term among cash register collectors used to describe the first register models ever produced by the re-formed corporate entity, The National Cash Register Company in 1885. These early wood registers had a deeper cash drawer than those to follow. The extra depth accommodated a sliding coin tray over the bill compartments identical to the earlier under-counter cash tills in popular use during the 1870's and 1880's.

Desk Autographic   A combination of cash drawer and manifolding autographic. The sale was written on the roll of paper through an opening in the top of the register. Then, after pressing a combination lock, a lever was pulled forward which rang a bell, opened the cash drawer, and moved the paper forward on a spool which was under lock and key. Some used multi-part paper which allowed a copy to be given as a receipt to the customer.

Detail Adder   A counter arrangement used on many early registers and on low-priced versions of later registers. Usually, two counter wheels per key cumulated either the number of key presses for that key or the cash values represented by the key. These simple mechanisms needed no linkage between every key and a single cash-totalling adder. The proprietor, therefore, had to add across the detail-adder wheels at the end of each day.

Devil's Head Pull   see Patterson Pull.

Dial   In cash register terminology, "dial" usually refered to a style of register that used a rotating clock-like face for indication such as the Kruse dial total adder or the National 110-principle dial register. Another register called "the Dial" operated completely differently.

Division   A section of keys in a register in which keys were segregated into multiple groupings. On some total-adding machines, divisions had individual counters. On others, special symbols were printed next to the sales amount on the detail strip. On detail adders, divisions were used to segregate ring-ups for various sections of a store. Colors were used to differentiate the keys in different divisions of a register.

Double Bank   A term used for an NCR 79-principle register (and 400 and 500 class) where a double row of keys made up the first key bank. The double bank was used when odd-cent keys were eliminated and all values less than $1.00 were contained in the double bank, thereby leaving the remaining banks to accomplish higher ring-ups. "DB" was added to the model number to designate this feature.

Drawer-powered   A principle of operation for a register where the action of pushing in an open cash drawer stored up energy in various springs to power the next registration with no power stroke required on the keys or crank. This method was invented by Hallwood and subsequently used in NCR's registers in the 1000 class.

Drawer Pull   A handle or other protrusion on the front of the cash drawer of a register used to pull the drawer open in the event the drawer spring broke or when the drawer was especially full of coins, causing it to open only partially. As spring steel improved, springs seldom broke and drawer pulls became obsolete.

Electric illumination   Electric illumination was an option, but only on NCR electric-motor-powered registers. The earlier form consisted of a light bulb in a brass holder that lit up the indication during registration, the duration being controlled by a timer. A later optional version was a bronze-framed glass top sign housing a bulb that lit up a message etched in the glass when registration was made. Usually, one substituted for the other on a register. Either one makes a register more collectible.

Electro   see Electrotype.

Electrotype   A customized printing block (also called an "electro") that could be added optionally to some NCR register printers. The print surface was made by NCR by pressure molding the customer-specified design with a temporary molding material. Then a thin, hard shell was electrodeposited on the print surface, the mold was removed and the thin shell was backed by lead to complete the block.

Extended Base   A register case style created from the need to have a larger cash drawer than would match up physically with the sides of a smaller register. The result was an extended base, which often made for an attractive result.

Finger Rail   see Rail.

Flash   A stamped sheet-metal cover usually painted red which popped up to cover a register's indicators from view while a new registration was being made. This was actually a security feature preventing the sly clerk from performing a partial registration that might have the indicators show a correct value from a previous transaction while the counters added a lower value. The clerk in that instance could pocket the difference. The flash forced the clerk to complete the registration before any indication was displayed.

Floor Cabinet see Floor Model.

Floor Model NCR and Hallwood may have been the only manufacturers of a floor-model version of cash registers. These were self-contained register stands with multiple drawers controlled from the register.

Improved A term used by NCR to mean a register with certain features available as standard equipment. For example, improvements on a 300-Class register were flash, customer counter, lid counter, key lock, detachable resetting key, glass top, marble slab, proprietor's name in the top sign, and velvet-lined lid.

Indicators Tabs on which numerals were impressed or imprinted corresponding to key values. The press of a key caused the appropriate indicator to come into view. There were various styles of indicators, including the common pop-up kind, the roller indicator, dials, etc.

This display of the amount registered was the key to allowing the customer to audit the clerk's honesty. The feature dates all the way back to Ritty's early machines.

Indicator Flash see Flash.

Indicator Housing The glass and metal or wood top of a register that enclosed the indicators, yet left the most recent registration clearly in view.

Initial Keys Separating transactions according to clerk was accomplished by assigning letters to each clerk and requiring their pressing the appropriate initial key along with the sale amount. Usually, initial keys had all or a part of a bank to themselves.

Key Arrester When one key of a register had been started, this device made it impossible to operate any other key until the key started was pushed all the way down and the registration completed.

Key Bank A row of keys, usually a vertical row.

Key Check The surface of a key in which the key value was displayed. There were many different kinds of key checks including nickel silver with impressed numerals, glass, brass, etc.

Key Index A term used by NCR to refer to a device consisting of a curved metal plate with openings for inserting pieces of cardboard. With it a merchant could make the initial keys represent any special transactions desired.

Key Lock A device which made it either possible or impossible, as desired, to operate the register with the cash drawer open.

Key Stem The metal lever on which the key check sat.

Knocker A term used by NCR in the 1890's. A knocker was a register that was built by NCR specifically to compete with some other manufacturer's machine. Some knockers bore remarkable resemblance to the target machine and were used to intimidate the competitor into selling out or ceasing business. Other knockers were repriced Nationals with a few less important features missing to justify the lower price.

Lever In cash register terminology, a lever was specifically the lever used on machines that used a principle similar to the Ideal. Instead of vertical key banks, a lever would be moved up and down a leverway. Click stops associated with numerals would facilitate leaving the lever at the desired position to be registered.

Lid The cover enclosing the counters in many press-down key registers. The lid was usually lockable.

Lid Counter More secure registers provided a counter to tell how many times the lid was raised. The lid counter is never resettable and is usually mounted with solder-filled screw heads.

Locks One lock locked the lid of the register, which covered the adding mechanism. Another locked the registering keys so that they could not be operated or the cash drawer opened—"handy in case you are alone in the store at any time and want to leave it for a few minutes." There were other locks peculiar to each type of register—some to cover the print mechanism, others for special counting wheels, etc.

Manifolding Autographic Fancy boxes which presented a portion of a roll of paper to the operator for hand writing of bills. Usually they handled multi-part forms with one part rolling up inside the box as an audit trail. NCR suggested that they be used as a suggestion box or that physicians use them for writing out prescriptions.

Marble-Adding Register   This term referred mainly to the Simplex and Sun registers which used clay marbles that key action released into enumerated troughs for manual summation at the end of the day.

Marble Slab   see Slab.

Model Number   Most register companies used model numbers to differentiate models within their product line. The practice began with the National Manufacturing Company and was continued by Patterson and others. There was some identification of features in many of the model numbering systems, but collectors should use them with caution since their application was not fully systematized.

The NCR class model numbering system was the closest to a reliable system, but even it became jumbled and was used inconsistently between earlier and later machines as features increased and changed.

Multiple Cash Drawers   Both table model and floor model style registers were designed to accommodate multiple cash drawers, usually one per clerk and up to a maximum of nine drawers in a floor model. These were part of a system to segregate performance by clerk or salesperson. Cash drawers could be operated only by pressing the proper keys on the register, which forced a properly segregated recording to be made.

Name Plate   Some registers had two-piece lids so that the center portion (the name plate) could be a custom casting with the name of the proprietor or establishment. Top signs and backs of registers were alternate choices for customizing.

Nickel Silver   An alloy of nickel and silver sometimes called "German silver." This metal was often used for early cash register key checks since they did not require lacquering as did brass.

"No Sale"   A cash register key and indicator used to open the cash drawer without registering an amount. For security reasons, the "No Sale" key usually had its own counter.

Number Printer   A printer option for NCR 400- and 500-Class registers. A small box with six or more small levers was mounted on the slip printer of the register. The operator set the levers by hand to a desired value and that value would be printed on the slip along with the standard printer information such as cash amount. Printers using wider paper were required for this feature.

"Paid Out"   A special key which usually threw out the main adder and caused some special mark to be printed. More advanced registers had a counter for this key since the value represented cash taken from the cash drawer.

Paper Punch   A primitive means for perforating. A roll of paper about as wide as the register and ruled to correspond with the key spacing was located inside the register. Each key press would punch a hole in the corresponding column of the paper and advance the roll, making a permanent record as would a detail adder. The proprietor counted column totals and performed all arithmetic manually to obtain a daily cash total.

Patent Tag   In cash registers, the patent tag or plate refers to a tag attached to the register that lists the most recent numbers of patents granted which are associated with the machine. The patent tag may also contain the model number.

Patterson Pull   A nickname developed at NCR for the drawer pull that appears similar to the "Face of the North Wind" used often as a design motif on turn-of-the-century furniture.

Pinch Lever   A lever used on NCR 500-class machines that required pinching in order to move it to a new clerk's initial or other special function. The lever actually rotated a wheel of counters so that the appropriate clerk or special function total adder was engaged and in view.

Premium Register   A low-priced cash register produced by some manufacturers to compete with NCR's dominance in a new way. Premium registers were sold to cigar distributors, for example, for bundling with a quantity of cigars. The gimmick was if a bar bought the cigars, they wouldn't have to pay for a register.

Press-down Key Register   The most popular style of register originally conceived by Ritty. The act of pressing down a key powered the various register functions.

Principle   A word brought into popular use in the register field by NCR in 1892 when its total adders were introduced. A "principle" of operation meant its unique mechanical design. For example, the 79 principle used a shaft-driven crank-powered mechanism whereas the 35 principle used a modular press-down key approach.

Printer   A device which could be set mechanically to print on paper the sale amount, electrotypes or other words and text. In the case of the sale amount, the mechanism consisted of wheels similar to counters, but with raised numerals that were inked for printing.

Pull   see Drawer Pull.

Pull-down Key   A keying approach similar to press-down keys but requiring that the keys be pulled. This may have required less finger power. It is found on the Bensinger, Gem, and early NCR 35-principle machines, to name a few.

Purse   All NCR 300-, 400- and 500-classes equipped with multiple drawers were equipped with large purses, one for each drawer; they were used by clerks in turning over to the proprietor money received during the day. Small purses were furnished one for each drawer in which the proprietor placed change to be used by clerk.

Rail, Railing   The rail was mounted on the till cover in early registers to assist holding the register steady as the cash drawer was pushed closed. Early machines were wood and were too light to resist moving against a good push. The use of heavier metal-cased machines eventually made the rail obsolete.

Receipt   A paper note handed to the customer giving evidence of the sale of goods. Receipts were handwritten or printed by the register or both.

"Received on Account"   A special key used to indicate that cash was received to apply against a charge account. Even when the "Charge" key was set up to throw out the main adder, this key never did since cash receipts were involved. Printers marked these transactions distinctively on paper and the bigger registers had a separate adder.

Registration   This is the main function of a cash register. Registration is the act of logging and retaining a record of the occurrence of the receipt of cash. Registering could occur merely by punching a hole in a piece of paper as in the early paper punches. It could also mean adding the sale to a counter that could be reconciled against the drawer contents at the end of the day. Finally, it could mean both counting and printing on various strips, stubs, checks or slips for later recall. Even the Autographic registers were called registers because they retained a record of the sale.

Ring-Up   1. Another word for registering a sale. 2. The value of a sale as in "this register rings up to $10.00."

Roller Indicators   See Indicators.

Sales Printer   A printer that produced a detail strip of paper rolled up into the register thereby recording and retaining all transactions in sequence. Also called a "detail strip printer."

Sales Slip   Refers to a receipt that is bigger than a check and that could contain more information, both printed and handwritten. Often sales slips started in order books that were filled out and totalled by hand before the customer total was keyed into the register.

Saloon Register   This is usually a register with key values beginning at 5¢ and has no odd cent keys.

Secret Total   An obscure NCR feature where a register was equipped with two total adders, one operating normally and turned back to zero at the end of each day. The other was tied up and couldn't be reset. The latter counter was kept under a locked lid. Both were advanced by the amount of each registration. The secret total gave a running cumulative tally since the register's activation.

Shipping Label Refers to the label used by NCR to designate model number, serial number, date and destination of first shipment and occasionally a few other items of information. These labels are usually glued behind or underneath the register drawer.

Slab A marble slab used as a till cover on which a coin could be bounced to detect slugs by their ring. Slabs were smooth and eased the pushing of coins off the slab edge into the correct cash drawer compartment below.

Slip Printer An optional printer that imprinted the registered sale and other optional customized information on a slip inserted manually. The slip was a separate piece of paper for each sale.

Small Machine Usually any register of 15 keys or less; see Candy Store Register.

Special Keys Added register functions were provided with special keys such as "Charge" and "Paid Out." These keys caused special indication to show up, special characters to print via the various printers. In some cases, special keys caused the corresponding sale value to be omitted from the main total adder (i.e. to be "thrown out") while being added in to a special counter associated with that key.

Stub A check with a subdivided portion that was intended to be torn off. The printer actually perforated across the check so the stub would tear off easily. Usually, stub printers were used with cashier systems where the cashier tore off and retained the stub. The sale amount was printed twice—on the check and the stub.

Tape Holder A term used by NCR to describe a fancy canister (6" diameter standard, 12" optional) encasing check printer paper for 500-Class machines. The reel was hung on the upper right of the 500-class register giving it a distinctive appearance and increasing the printer capacity. Registers with the larger tape holders are highly collectible. American also had some register models with this type of canister.

Throw Out A phrase used by NCR referring to a mechanical option on some registers where a key press did not add into the total adder. For example, some registers were ordered with the "Charge" key to "throw out" the main adder so that charge transactions would not mix in with the cash totals. Except for theft, the cash drawer contents always tallied with the adder.

Tied-up Counter A counter that could not be turned to zero, such as most lid counters.

Time Recorder A clock option mounted on high-grade registers. The earlier clock made by Waterbury was round and was mounted in various places, such as the side of the lid, the side of the register, even on the top sign. The clock was wound and set by the proprietor in the evening before closing the store. When the clerk arrived in the morning, he touched the spring and the recorder would indicate at once the time of opening. The clock is ornamental and adds to the beauty of the register.

A slightly later clock made by Seth Thomas was bigger and included a time printer. It was a highly desirable option on 500-class machines. The clerk could stamp the time on receipts, slips or even a time card by inserting them and manually hitting the print wheel through the inker and to the paper.

Top Sign A sign prevalent on most registers that either called attention to the register, instructed the patron to "Get a Receipt" or advertised the proprietor's name. Top signs could be individually customized for a small extra fee ($1 or $2). They are often missing from registers found in the rough, but appropriate replacements are available. Specific register types require specific top signs to preserve authenticity. All top signs shown in these volumes are correct for the registers on which they appear; however there may have been alternate signs equally appropriate in some cases. NCR discontinued the use of top signs in 1915.

Total Adder A register mechanism that channeled all key press values into one main counter leaving no manual summation required at the end of the day. The Incorruptible Cashier used a total adder first in 1879-80 followed by the Kruse dial register in 1885-6. Multiple total adders were also used on 500-Class NCR machines to cumulate cash totals for each clerk.

Turn-to-zero Counter   A counter that could be reset to zero.

Under-key Check Printer   A device used on NCR press-down key machines as an option that printed sales amounts on a check that would be manually inserted under the keys. Except for the ribbon spool holders and the ruled metal guide that extended across the back of the till cover under the keys, this printer was almost invisible.

Unimproved   A term used by NCR to mean registers without improvements such as under-lid velvet, marble slab, etc. See "Improved."

Bibliography

Allyn, Stanley C. *My First 50 Years in Dayton*. Dayton, Ohio: Winters National Bank and Trust Co., 1963.

Bashe, Charles J., Lyle R. Johnson, John H. Palmer, and Emerson W. Pugh. *IBM's Early Computers*. Edited by I. Bernard Cohen, assoc. ed. William Aspray. Cambridge, Mass.: The MIT Press, 1986.

Boorstin, Daniel J. *The American: The Democratic Experience*, Vol. 3, New York: Vintage Books, 1974.

Bueschel, Richard. *The Illustrated Guide to the 100 Most Collectible Trade Stimulators*. 2 vol. Wheatridge, Colorado: The Coin Slot, 1978.

"The Cash Recording Machine." *Scientific American* 38 (February 16, 1878):cover story.

Conover, Charlotte Reeve. *Builders in New Fields*. New York: G. P. Putnam's Sons, 1939.

Crowther, Samuel. *John H. Patterson, Pioneer in Industrial Welfare*. New York: Doubleday Page & Co., 1923.

"Daley's Safety Money Drawer." *Scientific American* 72 (June 1, 1895):340.

Fey, Marshall. *Slot Machines*. Las Vegas, Nevada: Nevada Publications, 1983.

"Fuller Cash Carrier." *Scientific American* 62 (March 15, 1890): 115.

Fuller, Frederick L. *My Half Century As An Inventor*. New York: n.p., 1938.

Kaempffert, Waldemar. *A Popular History of American Inventors*. New York: Charles Scribner & Sons, 1924.

Marcossen, Isaac F. *Colonel Deeds, Industrial Builder*. New York: Dodd, Mead & Co., 1947.

_____. *Wherever Men Trade: The Romance of the Cash Register*. New York: Dodd, Mead & Co., 1945.

"Mechanical Cashier." *Scientific American* supplement (February 21, 1903).

National Cash Register Company. Catalogues for 1892, 1898, 1902, 1908, 1909, and 1915. Dayton, Ohio: The National Cash Register Co.

_____. *U. S. Price List of National Cash Registers No. 29*. Dayton, Ohio: The National Cash Register Co., April 19, 1907.

_____. *U. S. Price List of National Cash Registers, no. 38*. Dayton, Ohio: The National Cash Register Co., July 1, 1915.

Terry, Samuel H. *How to Keep A Store*. New York: Fowler & Wells, 1884.

Time-Life Encyclopedia of Collectibles. Buttons to Chess Sets. New York: Time-Life Books, Inc., 1978.

Court Cases

National Cash Register v. American Cash Register. (C.C.E.D.Pa. 1890) (Nos. 61 and 62).

National Cash Register v. Boston Cash Indicator and Recorder. (C.C.D.Mass. 1891) (Nos. 2405 and 2542).

National Cash Register v. Boston Cash Indicator and Recorder. (U.S. 1895) (No. 155).

National Cash Register v. Boston Cash Indicator and Recorder. (C.C.D.Mass. 1898) (No. 2619).

National Cash Register v. Century Cash Register and William T. McGraw. (C.C.E.D.Mich. 1904).

National Cash Register v. Globe Cash Register. (C.C.E.D.Mich. 1904).

National Cash Register v. Hallwood Cash Register. (C.C.S.D.Ohio 1897) (No. 808).

National Cash Register v. Michael Heintz. (C.C.E.D.Mich. 1895)

National Cash Register v. Hubinger-Carroll Cash Register. (C.C.D.Conn. 1913) (No. 807).

National Cash Register v. Ideal Cash Register. (C.C.D.N.J. 1902).

National Cash Register v. Kruse Cash Register. (C.C.S.D.N.Y. 1892).

National Cash Register v. Lamson Consolidated Store Service. (C.C.D.N.J. 1891).

National Cash Register v. Navy Cash Register, Paul E. Berger and Luke Cooney, Jr. (C.C.N.D.Ill. 1899) (No. 25351).

National Cash Register v. Navy Cash Register. (C.C.N.D.Ill. 1900).

National Cash Register v. New Columbus Watch Co. (C.C.S.D.Ohio 1897) (No. 807).

National Cash Register v. Sun Manufacturing Co., Winfield S. Courtright, William A. Gill and Thomas A. Morton. (C.C.S.D.Ohio 1904) (No. 1224).

National Cash Register v. Union Computing Machine Co. (C.C.D.N.J. 1904).

National Cash Register Co. v. Union Computing Machine Co. (3rd Cir. 1904) (No. 933).

U.S. v. National Cash Register. (C.C.S.D.Ohio 1912) (Criminal No. 382), (6th Cir. 1915).

Index

Index of Illustrations

THE INCORRUPTIBLE CASHIER

Composed by Eastern Graphics in 11 point Zapf Book Light,
2 points leaded, with display lines in Zapf Chancery Bold.
Cover design by James Weaver Graphic Design